Gift

D0297243

Off-the-road
Wheeled and Combined
Traction Devices

275156

Ag TT 85-1-1122

# Off-the-road Wheeled and Combined Traction Devices

## Theory and Calculation

[*Vezdekhodnye Kolesnye i Kombinirovannye
Dvizhiteli (Teoriia i Raschet)*]

TL
235.6
A43

Ia.S. Ageikin

*Translated from Russian*

Amerind Publishing Co. Pvt. Ltd., New Delhi
1987

Mashinostroenie Publishers
Moscow, 1972

© 1987 Oxonian Press Pvt. Ltd., New Delhi

Translated and published under an agreement for the
United States Department of Agriculture, Washington, D.C., by
Amerind Publishing Co. Pvt. Ltd., 66 Janpath, New Delhi 110 001


Translator: Prof. A. Jaganmohan
General Editor: Dr. V.S. Kothekar


Published and printed at Printsman Press, Faridabad, India

UDC 629.1.02

The topics covered in this book include the operating conditions of off-the-road vehicles, the theory of interaction between wheeled vehicles and the deformable surfaces over which they move and the influence of design and operating parameters of the vehicles on the mobility as well as other properties of the machines.

Methods of determining the basic parameters of off-the-road vehicles have been elaborated.

This book is intended for engineers specializing in automobile construction. It will also be useful for scientific personnel engaged in the design of automobiles with a high maneuverability.

# Preface

The automobile is, at present, the most widely used means of mass transport on road (a surface specially prepared for plying vehicles). When there are no roads, cargo can be transported by crawler tracked vehicles, which have been devised for this purpose. However, vast areas exist in which combined transport vehicles can be utilized on both paved surfaces as well as off-the-road. Neither the usual automobile nor a crawler tracked machine is an effective means of transport for mixed conditions. It is in this sphere that automobiles of an improved design and high mobility become most effective.

It is the type of the vehicle which, above all, determines its suitability for either paved surfaces or off-the-road conditions, or for limited off-the-road transportation. A vehicle designed for use in a variety of road–soil conditions is designated as an off-the-road vehicle.

Naturally, such a machine cannot compete with vehicles specially designed for use on paved roads or with tracked vehicles intended for off-the-road conditions. The suitability of a vehicle for one or the other of the above must correspond to the relative frequency with which the automobile is utilized under such circumstances.

It has been observed that highly mobile off-the-road vehicles are mostly used on paved roads, even when the road network is not well-developed. With a further growth of an extensive roadway system, the frequency with which these vehicles are run on roads will increase even more. Hence, a necessary requirement of off-the-road vehicles is that their performance on highways should be of a high order. Such vehicles must also be capable of effective utilization under a variety of off-the-road conditions. A vehicle's requirements are different for different off-the-road conditions, which often may deviate from each other. For instance, when an automobile is to be used on dirt roads, it is advisable to equip it with tires having widely spaced treads; while for sandy tracks, the treads should be more closely spaced. When a vehicle is to move over waterlogged land, the pressure exerted over the soil must be very small; while for hard surfaces with viscous mud layers, the pressure exerted could be higher, etc.

Considering the fact that the requirements of a vehicle for dissimilar conditions must vary, it follows that an optimal combination of such condition must be obtained. To solve this problem, it is necessary to know the mechanical properties of all soil surfaces and the frequency with which an automobile passes over them, the laws governing the interaction between the motion of wheeled vehicles with such surfaces and the influence of design and operating parameters on their effective usage under deviating conditions.

In the history of automobiles, for more than half a century wheeled vehicles have been continuously improved for better performance on metalled roads. Various theories have been evolved for the interaction between the road and the wheels of a vehicle in order to assess their performance as a function of the parameters of the vehicle and the road.

Problems related to the interaction between a wheeled vehicle and the deformation of ground surfaces have not been investigated to a very large extent. This may be due to several reasons. Firstly, it can be attributed to the complexity of the problem, which is related to the deformability of the two bodies (tire and ground) in contact with each other and the exceptionally diverse and unstable mechanical properties of the ground surfaces. Secondly, it could be due to the fact that the solution of this problem is linked with two separate sciences: the theory of automobiles and that of soil mechanics, each of which is, most often, separately dealt with by specialists of either automobile theory or of soil mechanics.

Investigations relating to the passage of wheeled machines over soft soils took a sharp jump in the fifties, due to the research work of V.F. Babkov, A.K. Birulya, N.A. Ul'yanov, G.B. Bezborodov and others. The development and coordination of these works was largely due to the active involvement of the Committee headed by G.V. Zimelev, set up at the Institute of Complex Transport Problems, Academy of Sciences, USSR to look into the problems of the motion of wheeled machines.

A considerable amount of work in this field is being carried out abroad, of which the investigations of M. Bekker deserve particular attention.

These investigations have resulted in the accumulation of extensive theoretical and experimental data on the interaction between pneumatic wheels and deformable soil surfaces. New types of tires have been developed, such as tires with adjustable pressure, arched tires, wide profile tires, pneumatic wheels, giant tires, etc. The performance of such tires has been investigated on different ground surface conditions.

The effectiveness of the utilization of modern high performance automobiles on off-the-road travel has increased significantly. However, the possibilities for a further improvement in the effectiveness of wheeled machines under a combination of paved and unpaved road conditions are far from exhausted. No conclusive theory has yet been reached for determining the functional relationship between the parameters of ground surfaces, vehicles and the travel conditions of off-the-road wheeled vehicles and secondly, there is a paucity of statistical data regarding the mechanical properties of ground surfaces.

An attempt has been made in this book to lay a foundation for the theory of off-the-road wheeled vehicles acceptable for various types of tires and the principal types of road–soil surfaces. The theory is derived from the basic principles governing the deformation of ground surfaces and pneumatic tires. Based on this, the interaction between a single pneumatic wheel and the ground surface is investigated, and the effect of the structural parameters of the wheel on the effectiveness of its utilization, under different conditions, is analyzed. Specific features involved in the interaction between a multiwheeled vehicle and the ground surface have been considered, and the influence of such interaction parameters on the performance of the automobile has been studied. Investigations are being conducted into the possibility of improving the versatility of the vehicle by combining several types of vehicles.

The book finally concludes with a method for determining the basic parameters of off-the-road wheeled vehicles.

Although it was not possible to avoid making substantial assumptions while studying the interaction between those bodies distinguished by the complex nature of deformation, all the chapters in this book are provided with the maximum possible experimental data obtained by the author or gathered from various sources in scientific literature.

# Contents

PREFACE ... vii

LIST OF SYMBOLS ... xiii

CHAPTER 1. MECHANICAL PROPERTIES OF SOIL
AND SNOW-COVERED SURFACES FOR
VEHICULAR TRANSPORT ... 1

Characteristics of the Principal Types of Soils ... 1

Soil Resistance to Normal Loads ... 8

Resistance of Soil to Shear Load ... 22

CHAPTER 2. WHEEL–SOIL INTERACTION ... 31

Physical Processes Occurring when a Wheel Rolls
over Soil ... 31

Special Features of Pneumatic Wheel–Soil Interaction ... 33

Analytical Treatment of the Interaction between an
Elastic Wheel and the Soil ... 46

A Simplified Method of Determining Tire–Soil
Interaction ... 69

The Parameters for Evaluating the Working Conditions
of a Wheel ... 73

CHAPTER 3. THE EFFECT OF WHEEL PARAMETERS
ON PERFORMANCE ... 79

Effect of Tire Dimensions ... 79

Effect of the Tire Profile Shape ... 87

Effect of Tread Design ... 98

Effect of Inflation Pressure ... 106

Effect of Vertical Load . . . 114

A Comparative Study of the Performance of Various
Types of Tires . . . 117

CHAPTER 4. ANALYSIS OF MULTIWHEELED AND
COMBINED TRACTION VEHICLES . . . 129

The Rolling of a Wheel over a Single Track . . . 129

Effect of Axle Number on Vehicle Performance . . . 132

Load Distribution over the Axles . . . 138

Effect of Kinematic Wheel Imbalance on the
Performance of a Multiaxled Vehicle . . . 146

Special Features of Wheel–Soil Interaction of a
Multiwheeled Vehicle . . . 149

Comparative Evaluation of the Arrangement of
Multiaxled Vehicles . . . 156

Combined Traction Vehicles . . . 160

CHAPTER 5. DETERMINATION OF THE PRINCIPAL
PARAMETERS OF OFF-THE-ROAD
VEHICLES . . . 176

Classes and Systems of Design Calculations . . . 176

Initial Design Data from Road-Soil Conditions . . . 178

Method of Determining Vehicle Parameters . . . 183

REFERENCES . . . 197

# List of Symbols

| | |
|---|---|
| $A$ | total work done on tire, kg·m |
| $A'$ | soil compression parameter, kg/cm² |
| $A_e$ | work done to overcome tire-wall elasticity, kg·m |
| $A_p$ | potential energy of deflection, kg·m/s |
| $A_{ps}$ | potential energy of sidewall deflection, kg·m/s |
| $A_{pt}$ | potential energy of tread deflection, kg·m/s |
| $A_r$ | work done on rubber, kg·m |
| $B$ | soil parameter characterizing the effect of load duration on deformation |
| $B$ | profile width, cm |
| $B'$ | soil rupture parameter |
| $B_F$ | width of rim, cm |
| $b$ | width of plate (ram), cm |
| $b$ | width of contact patch, cm |
| $b_e$ | equivalent width of contact, cm |
| $b_s$ | width of sidewall over contact zone, cm |
| $b_t$ | width of tread, cm |
| $b_w$ | contact width, cm |
| $C$ | soil parameter |
| $c_0$ | internal cohesion of soil, kg/cm² |
| $c_p$ | rigidity of suspension |
| $D$ | outer diameter of tire, cm |
| $d$ | diameter of plate (ram), cm |
| $d$ | diameter of rim, cm |
| $E$ | modulus of soil deformation, kg/cm² |
| $E'$ | modulus of soil shear, kg/cm² |
| $E_d$ | dynamic modulus of deformation, kg/cm² |
| $E_r$ | modulus of rubber rigidity, kg/cm² |

xiv

| | |
|---|---|
| $F$ | area of plate (ram), cm$^2$ |
| $F$ | tire-soil contact area, cm$^2$ |
| $f$ | coefficient of resistance to motion |
| $f_b$ | resistance to bulldozing effect, kg |
| $f_c$ | resistance to compaction effect, kg |
| $f_f$ | coefficient of static friction |
| $f_g$ | coefficient of soil resistance to motion |
| $f_s$ | coefficient of sliding friction |
| $f_t$ | resistance to tire deformation, kg |
| $G_w$ | vertical load on wheel, kg |
| $H$ | height of tire profile, cm |
| $H_s, H_s$ | depth of soft soil layer, cm |
| $H_t$ | depth of turf layer, cm |
| $h$ | depth of rut (sinkage of plate), cm |
| $h_t$ | deflection of tread, cm |
| $h_t$ | height of tread arch, cm |
| $i$ | ground shear |
| $K_\tau$ | soil parameter |
| $K'_\tau$ | soil displacement parameter |
| $k_t$ | pressure at tire-soil contact (governed by the rigidity of the carcass), kg/cm$^2$ |
| $L$ | tire-soil contact length at the outer profile, cm |
| $L_w$ | contact length, cm |
| $l$ | contact length in the flat zone, cm |
| $l_s$ | arc length, cm |
| $M_r$ | retarding moment, kg·m |
| $M_w$ | turning moment at the wheel, kg·m |
| $m$ | saturation coefficient of tread pattern |
| $N$ | power expended on rolling, kg·m/s |
| $N$ | number of axles |
| $N, N_1$ | tensile force, kg |
| $N_a$ | power expended on soil adhesion, kg·m/s |
| $N_g$ | power expended on soil deformation, kg·m/s |
| $N_s$ | power expended on slippage, kg·m/s |
| $N_t$ | power expended on radial deformation of tires, kg·m/s |
| $N_\alpha$ | power expended on overcoming gradient, kg·m/s |
| $N_\tau$ | power expended on tangential deformation of tire, kg·m/s |

| $O$ | instantaneous center |
|---|---|
| $P$ | force, kg |
| $P_a$ | specific resistance of rubber sheet to detachment, kg |
| $P_a$ | wheel–soil adhesion force, kg |
| $P_{ch}$ | tractive force of chains, kg |
| $P_e$ | overall efficiency of wheel |
| $P_f$ | rolling resistance, kg |
| $P_{fa}$ | resistance due to adhesion, kg |
| $P_{fg}$ | rolling resistance of soil, kg |
| $P_{ft}$ | rolling resistance due to tire deformation, kg |
| $P_s$ | sinkage parameter |
| $P_s$ | lateral drift |
| $p$ | pressure, kg/cm$^2$ |
| $p_s$ | specific pressure resisting the stripping of a rubber sheet, kg/cm$^2$ |
| $p_w$ | tire inflation pressure, kg/cm$^2$ |
| $Q, Q'$ | external load, kg |
| $q_0$ | pressure corresponding to initial density of soil, kg/cm$^2$ |
| $q_s, q_{so}$ | load bearing capacity of soil, kg/cm$^2$ |
| $q$ | average pressure on soil, kg/cm$^2$ |
| $R$ | outer radius of tire, cm |
| $R_a$ | radius of center of turning, cm |
| $R_r$ | rolling radius of wheel, cm |
| $R_s$ | soil reaction, kg |
| $R_w$ | rolling radius, cm |
| $R_{wo}$ | radius of pure rolling, cm |
| $r_r$ | tread-band radius, cm |
| $r_s$ | sidewall radius, cm |
| $S_p$ | perimeter, cm |
| $s$ | path traversed by tread, cm |
| $T, T_s$ | tractive force, kg |
| $t$ | pitch of cleats or lugs, cm |
| $t'$ | soil property parameter |
| $t_s$ | temperature of surroundings, °C |
| $t_t$ | temperature of tire, °C |
| $u'$ | soil property parameter |
| $v$ | speed, m/s |
| $v_{per}$ | permissible speed, kmph |

| | |
|---|---|
| $v_t$ | volume occupied by tire, $cm^3$ |
| $v_t'$ | specific volume occupied by tire, $cm^3/kg$ |
| $v_w$ | volume occupied by wheel, $cm^3$ |
| $W$ | width of tire profile, cm |
| $W_r$ | width of wheel rim, cm |
| $W_w$ | wind resistance, kg |
| $w_0$ | moisture content, % |
| $z$ | depth of submergence in soil, cm |
| $z$ | distance from elementary layer under consideration, cm |

## Greek Letters

| | |
|---|---|
| $\alpha$ | ground stress damping coefficient |
| $\alpha_c$ | angle between contact surface and the horizontal, deg |
| $\alpha_s$ | sidewall arc angle, deg |
| $\alpha_w$ | angle, deg |
| $\beta$ | angle between elementary vector of soil reaction at the point of contact and the vertical, deg |
| $\beta_a$ | sidewise listing angle, deg |
| $\beta_c'$ | crown angle, deg |
| $\gamma$ | density of soil, $g/cm^3$ |
| $\Delta$ | height of cleats or lugs, cm |
| $\Delta_s$ | width of tread at the shoulder, cm |
| $\Delta_t$ | width of tread at the central portion of the contact patch, cm |
| $\delta$ | radial deformation of tire |
| $\delta_h$ | relative lateral deformation |
| $\delta_r$ | compression of rubber tread |
| $\delta_s$ | slip coefficient |
| $\delta_{sw}$ | deformation of sidewall |
| $\delta_t$ | deformation of treadband |
| $\eta$ | efficiency of driving wheel |
| $\lambda$ | $=(h/b)$ or $(h/D')$ |
| $\mu$ | soil parameter |
| $\xi$ | distance from wheel axis to soil surface, cm |
| $\rho$ | angle, deg |
| $\rho_w$ | kinematic imbalance |
| $\sigma$ | shear stress in soil, $kg/cm^2$ |

| | |
|---|---|
| $\tau$ | specific shear resistance of soil, $kg/cm^2$ |
| $\tau_r$ | specific friction force between rubber and soil |
| $\phi$ | angle of rotation, deg |
| $\phi$ | wheel–soil adhesion coefficient |
| $\phi_0$ | friction angle, deg |
| $\phi_r$ | coefficient of friction between rubber and soil |
| $\phi_s$ | angle of rotation for sidewall, deg |
| $\phi_{sl}$ | coefficient of sliding friction |
| $\phi_T$ | traction coefficient |
| $\phi_t$ | angle of rotation of tread, deg |
| $\psi$ | rigidity coefficient |
| $\psi_1$ | hysteresis loss coefficient |
| $\psi_2$ | internal friction coefficient |

# CHAPTER 1

# Mechanical Properties of Soil and Snow-covered Surfaces for Vehicular Transport

## CHARACTERISTICS OF THE PRINCIPAL TYPES OF SOILS

Surfaces for the movement of automobiles include highways with hard surfaces, dirt roads, natural soil and snow-covered surfaces. The suitability of these surfaces for automobile transport is governed by their evenness, deformability and frictional properties. On dry uneven surfaces, the effectiveness of the utilization of a machine depends primarily upon the quality of the suspension and the geometric parameters of the road. Deformable and slippery surfaces, however, are dependent upon the parameters interrelating the motion of the vehicle and the soil*.

In order to study deformation and frictional properties, transport surfaces may be subdivided into the following groups: motorable roads, cohesive soils, sandy soils, swamps and snow-covered surfaces.

Apart from their degree of evenness, motorable roads are characterized by their frictional properties, which are often estimated by the coefficient of adhesion between the tire and the road surface. The magnitude of the coefficient of adhesion is governed by the condition of the road surface (characterized by roughness, dirt, wetness or frost) and the type of tire.

Soil and snow fall under the category of dispersed solids. The principal difference between these and compact solids is that the solid particles in them do not form a continuous mass but occupy only a part of the volume. As a result the bonding strength between individual particles is considerably lower than the strength of the particles themselves. Under external loading, the individual particles first undergo displacement and shear.

The mechanical properties of soils are governed by their granulometric composition (i.e. size of solid particles), moisture content, density and peat cover. Granulometric composition is the most stable characteristic of soils and is often considered to be the basis for their classification. Moisture content, density and the turf cover vary widely during the course of a year due to weather conditions and human activity.

*Henceforth, for brevity, the term 'soil' shall be taken to represent all types of transport surfaces.

1

Soils which contain a large amount of clay particles are called cohesive soils.

Water, which is always present in soils, possesses different properties. With a slight increase in the moisture content of cohesive soils, water spreads throughout its entire mass in the form of a thin layer or fills up the fine capillary spaces between the soil particles. In such a state, water is characterized by negligible mobility, weak vaporization and is conducive to an increase in the cohesiveness of the soil.

When the amount of water in the soil increases, it fills up the larger pores and, as a result, the thickness of the water film over the soil particles increases. When the moisture content exceeds a certain level, which is characteristic for each type of soil, several properties of the soils undergo a sharp change. Hence, the state of cohesive soils is governed by their moisture content (consistency). The moisture content of a soil is often expressed as the ratio of the mass of water to the mass of dry soil.

Yield and plasticity limits are taken to be the characteristic factors which define soil consistency. The yield limit corresponds to that moisture content at which a slight increase in the latter transforms the soil into a fluid state. Stability under load conditions and cohesiveness of the soil become insignificant. The plasticity limit is defined by that moisture content at which the soil transforms from the plastic to the solid state. The difference between the yield and plasticity limits is known as the plasticity number. Types of cohesive soils of various granulometric compositions and plasticity numbers are given in Table 1.

**Table 1**

| Soil | Content of clay particles, % | Plasticity number |
|------|------------------------------|-------------------|
| Light loamy | 3–12 | 0–7 |
| Loamy | 12–18 | 7–10 |
| Heavy loamy | 18–25 | 10–15 |
| Clayey (argillaceous) | Above 25 | Above 15 |

When the moisture content of the soil exceeds the yield limit, conditions for automobile movement are at their worst. Such excessive soil moisture is typical in the spring, autumn and the rainy season, resulting in poor road conditions. During these periods, the depth of the waterlogged layer becomes quite significant. It may go up to 30 to 50 cm during the spring season at the end of the thaw, 20 to 30 cm during prolonged autumn rains and up to 10 cm during the short period rains of summer. During spring and autumn, bad conditions prevail for nearly three months in the forest areas and up to one and a half months in the steppes. The worst driving conditions for automobiles are the first few weeks after a thaw. A plastic condition of the cohesive soils is characteristic for the spring, autumn and rainy summer seasons, apart from the periods during which bad road conditions prevail.

Under these conditions, the mechanical properties of the soil are considerably influenced by the turf cover and the soil porosity. In the case of arable lands, the top layer of loose soil is 20 to 30 cm deep. When they are dry, cohesive soils possess sufficiently high mechanical properties.

The average values of the mechanical properties of cohesive soils of different compositions are given in Table 2.

Motion resistance increases when the soil is sticky. Data in scientific literature on the adhesiveness of soil is extremely meager. Adhesiveness of the soil may be estimated in terms of the specific force which must be applied to tear a lamina from the soil.

### Table 2

| Type of cohesive soil | Load bearing capacity of soil, $q_{s0}$, kg/cm$^2$ | Internal cohesion of soil, $c_0$, kg/cm$^2$ | Angle of friction in the soil, $\phi_0$, degrees | Modulus of deformation of soil, $E$, kg/cm$^2$ |
|---|---|---|---|---|
| Moisture content below plasticity limit | | | | |
| Light loamy | 3.5–7 | 0.5–1 | 24–25 | above 250 |
| Loamy | 4.5–9 | 0.6–1.2 | 21–23 | above 350 |
| Clayey | 5–10 and above | 0.75–1.5 | 15–20 | above 500 |
| Moisture content approximately equal to plasticity limit | | | | |
| Light loamy | 2.5–5 | 0.35–0.75 | 21–22 | up to 250 |
| Loamy | 3.5–6 | 0.4–0.8 | 18–20 | up to 350 |
| Clayey | 3.5–7 | 0.5–1.0 | 11–17 | up to 500 |
| Moisture content equal to 55–75 % of viscosity limit | | | | |
| Light loamy | 1–2.5 | 0.15–0.35 | 19–20 | up to 150 |
| Loamy | 1.75–3.0 | 0.25–0.4 | 16–18 | up to 200 |
| Clayey | 2.0–3.0 | 0.3–0.5 | 7–15 | 200–250 |
| Moisture content approximately equal to yield limit | | | | |
| Light loamy | 0.7–0.8 | 0.10–0.12 | 16–18 | 30–40 |
| Loamy | 0.6–0.9 | 0.10–0.15 | 12–15 | 30–40 |
| Clayey | 0.5–0.9 | 0.10–0.15 | 3–11 | 30–40 |
| Moisture content above yield limit | | | | |
| Light loamy | 0.3–0.6 | 0–0.05 | 10–16 | 3–9 |
| Loamy | 0.2–0.4 | 0.01–0.1 | 3–9 | 5–10 |
| Clayey | 0.1–0.3 | 0.03–0.1 | 0–6 | 10–15 |

The magnitude of adhesiveness varies as a function of the granulometric composition of the soil, particularly on its clay, humus and moisture content. Experimental data for the adhesiveness of soils are given in Table 3.

**Table 3**

| Soil | Adhesiveness in kg/cm$^2$ for various moisture ratios | | | | |
|---|---|---|---|---|---|
| | 0.7 | 0.8 | 0.9 | 1 | 1.1 |
| Sandy loam | 0.05 | 0.12 | 0.18 | 0.08 | 0.05 |
| Loess | 0.20 | 0.30 | 0.47 | 0.40 | 0.28 |
| Meadow bog | 0.14 | 0.23 | 0.45 | 0.54 | 0.38 |
| Chernozem (black soil) | 0.08 | 0.40 | 0.50 | 0.58 | 0.48 |

The properties of sandy (noncohesive) soils are far less dependent on the moisture content. With an increase of moisture, their resistance to the external load initially increases to some extent and, thereafter, reduces when the yield limit is reached. The composition of sandy soils is characterized by their density, which has a predominant influence on their mechanical properties. Soil density is estimated by its porosity or bulk mass. Depending upon the granulometric composition, sandy soils are subdivided as coarse-grained, medium-grained, fine-grained and silty or dusty soils.

Compared to cohesive soils, sandy soils are distinguished by a greater internal friction angle $\phi_0$ and by the almost total absence of any internal bonding force $c_0$. Preliminary data for the parameters governing the mechanical properties of sandy soils are given in Table 4.

**Table 4**

| Sandy soil | Coefficient of porosity | Angle of internal friction $\phi_0$, deg. | Internal bonding force $c_0$, kg/cm$^2$ |
|---|---|---|---|
| Coarse-grained | 0.41–0.5 | 43 | 0.02 |
| | 0.51–0.6 | 40 | 0.01 |
| | 0.61–0.7 | 38 | – |
| Medium-grained | 0.41–0.5 | 40 | 0.03 |
| | 0.51–0.6 | 38 | 0.02 |
| | 0.61–0.7 | 35 | 0.01 |
| Fine-grained | 0.41–0.5 | 38 | 0.06 |
| | 0.51–0.6 | 36 | 0.04 |
| | 0.61–0.7 | 32 | 0.02 |
| Silty (extremely fine) | 0.41–0.5 | 36 | 0.08 |
| | 0.51–0.6 | 34 | 0.06 |
| | 0.61–0.7 | 40 | 0.04 |

A poor quality of compactness distinguishes naturally occurring loose sands since settling, rather than pressure, changes the porosity of the sands. Hence, their deformation is principally due to shear. The modulus of deformation for such sands is quite large ($E > 50$ kg/cm$^2$). Their bearing capacity, in contrast to cohesive soils, is largely dependent upon the size of the body exerting pressure (plate), increasing with an increase in the size of the plate.

The bonding properties of sandy soils are governed by the internal friction angle. Fine-grained sands have the poorest bonding properties and load bearing capacities. Since the friction coefficient of rubber over sand is greater than the internal friction of the latter, ground shear occurs not at the point of contact of the plate with the soil but somewhat lower down.

The bearing capacity and bonding properties of sand, compared to cohesive soils, increase mainly in the presence of a neighboring solid (firm) layer.

The coefficient of the internal friction of sand depends on its compactness, which increases to some extent with the increasing density and thickness of the sand layer. When the sand layer is of a large depth, it does not shear at the surface of contact; but at a layer deeper down, where it is less compact.

Land surfaces with excessive moisture, covered with a turf layer of not less than 30 cm under moist conditions and greater than 20 cm under dry conditions, are known as swamps or marsh lands.

Tracts of land with excess moisture, which have either a turf cover of less than 30 cm or nothing at all, are known as waterlogged soils when moist.

Marshes have three characteristic features namely, excessive moisture, which causes the soil to be starved of air, the growth of hygrophilous vegetation and, thirdly, accumulation of organic materials, i.e. remains of animal and plant organisms (mainly the latter), forming a layer of peat.

Marsh lands are of three types:

1. Continuous marshes where the peat cover lies directly over the mineral bed.

2. Sapropelic marsh, where the peat crust lies under organic or semiorganic slime (sapropel).

3. Floating marshes where the peat crust floats on water.

Marshes and waterlogged tracts of land occupy considerable territory in the northern and central zones of Europe and Asia. Arctic swamps thaw to a small depth, often not more than 40 to 50 cm. Their mechanical properties may be compared with those of cohesive soils during the poor road conditions occurring in the spring.

In eastern and central Siberia, swamps occupy nearly 20% of the area, thawing to a depth of 35 to 45 cm during summer. In western Siberia, the area occupied by marsh lands is still greater.

The mechanical properties of waterlogged soils are determined in terms of strength and thickness of the peat cover.

The bearing capacity of sapropelic marshes does not exceed 0.2 to 0.3

kg/cm² when the thickness of the peat cover is less than 2.5 m. When this thickness exceeds 3.5 to 4 m, the sapropel does not practically have any influence on the load bearing capacity of the marsh.

Floating swamps are impassable when the peat cover is less than 5 to 6 m. The principal difference between peat and mineral soils during compaction is the extremely high shrinkage due to excessive porosity, the absence of lateral displacements and the appreciable influence of the shear resistance of peat at the perimeter of the plate.

In contrast to mineral soils, the bearing capacity of peat does not increase with the size of the plate; on the other hand, it decreases. This is explained by the fact that the bearing capacity of peat is governed by its resistance to shear at the periphery of the plate. For an increase in plate diameter, the area increase is proportional to its square; while the perimeter is directly proportional and, as a consequence, the bearing capacity reduces.

Figure 1 shows the relationship between the load bearing capacity of peat and the perimeter to the area ratio $S_p/F$ of the plate.

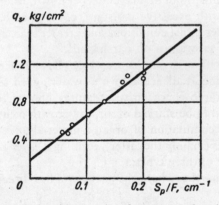

Fig. 1. Dependence of the bearing capacity of peat $q_s$ as a function of the perimeter to the area ratio $S_p/F$ of the plate.

As in the case of mineral soils, the bonding properties of the peat cover are characterized by the angle of internal friction $\phi_0$ and the internal bonding forces $c_0$.

The parameters defining the mechanical properties of swamps or marshes are shown in Table 5.

Virgin snow lands present considerable difficulties for the movement of land vehicles. Transport over snow is governed by the mechanical properties and depth of the snow cover. The mechanical properties of snow depend upon its density, structure, temperature and thickness.

The density of snow is defined by the ratio of the volume of water obtained from melted snow to that of the actual snow. As shown by numerous

**Table 5**

| Characteristic of peat cover | Thickness of peat cover, cm | Specific shear resistance of soil, $\tau$, kg/cm$^2$ | Modulus of deformation of soil, $E$, kg/cm$^2$ |
|---|---|---|---|
| Peat moss: | | | |
|   without undergrowth | 33.5–38.5 | 0.25–0.28 | 2.6–2.9 |
|   with undergrowth | 35–36 | 0.35–0.42 | 3.6–4.3 |
| Hypnum moss: | | | |
|   without undergrowth | 27–28 | 0.18–0.21 | 1.86–2.15 |
|   with undergrowth | 27 | 0.28–0.34 | 2.9–3.4 |
| Sedge cover: | | | |
|   with developed sedge clumps | 35–42 | 1.03–1.45 | 10.5–15.8 |
|   from interhillock depressions | 10–11 | 0.14–0.24 | 1.43–2.44 |
| Birch forest in interhillock depressions | 5–5.5 | 0.6–0.14 | 0.86–1.43 |
| Peat moss (35 to 40% decomposed; 180% moisture content) | — | 0.54 | 5.44 |
| Hypnum-sedge forest | 38–42 | 0.63–1 | 6.5–14 |
| Sedge-forest peat | — | 0.67 | 6.7 |

observations, the density of snow depends upon weather conditions, the severity of snowfall as well as the duration and conditions existing during the winter period. The monthly average density of snow continuously increases from the beginning to the end of the winter season. Its density sharply increases at the commencement of a thaw. Later when the snow becomes slushy, its density increases. When severe and continuous winds blow, the top layer becomes dense, which is known as the wind frozen crust.

The average density of freshly precipitated snow (according to Obolenskii) lies between 0.075 and 0.196 g/cm$^3$. The lower values are characteristic for low temperatures. The density of precipitated and wind compacted snow is 0.2 to 0.4 g/cm$^3$, while the density of drifting snow is 0.5 to 0.6 g/cm$^3$.

In Arctic regions, the density of multiseasonal snow is more than 0.6 g/cm$^3$.

The structure of snow varies under the action of wind, thaw, rain and the temperature of air.

Depending upon the structure of its flakes, snow is classified as fluffy, drifting or granular. Fluffy snow is characterized by large-sized flakes (5 to 6 mm) and low density (0.06 to 0.12 g/cm$^3$). It retains its original shape for only a short while. Drift snow has a diameter of 1 to 2 mm and a density of 0.2 g/cm$^3$ and above. As it melts, it transforms to a granular shape. Granular snow is formed from fluffy and drifting snow due to melting and recrystallization. It consists of an ice core of 3 to 4 mm diameter and has a density of

8

0.25 g/cm³ and above. The process of transformation of snow from one type to another is irreversible.

Snow cover thickness is the greatest in the Urals, Ob'-Enisei, Kamchatka-Chukotka and Primorsk regions, where it reaches 200 cm. In the northwestern and north European areas and mid-Siberian regions, the snow cover varies from 40 to 160 cm. In the central belt of the European part of the USSR, the thickness of snow varies from 30 to 100 cm, while in the western Kazakhstan and Trans-Baikal regions, it lies between 30 and 60 cm.

The relationship between snow deformation and the load impressed by a plate is analogous to that for soils. When the size of the plate is increased, the depth to which it sinks into the snow increases almost linearly (which is characteristic of soils with low internal friction). The bearing capacity of snow hardly variates with a change in the size of the plate due to the small magnitude of the internal friction angle.

The relationship between the shear resistance of snow and normal loading, in general, is far from linear (Fig. 2). This may be explained by the complex physicochemical processes which occur during snow deformation. However, in the range of loads specific for traction engines of a snowmobile (average pressure $q = 0.1–0.3$ kg/cm²), the relationship between the shear resistance of snow and normal loading may, with sufficient accuracy for practical purposes, assumed to be linear. This should be utilized for estimating the bonding properties of snow in terms of the same parameters as for soils, i.e. the coefficient of internal friction tan $\phi_0$ and internal bonding $c_0$.

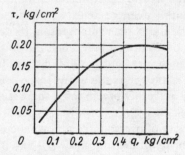

Fig. 2. The relationship between $\tau$ and $q$ for snow.

Parameters which characterize the mechanical properties of snow, depending upon its density and temperature, are given in Table 6.

## SOIL RESISTANCE TO NORMAL LOADS

### The Physical Pattern of Soil Deformation under Plate Indentation

For soils without a neighboring solid layer, the dependence of deformation $h$ due to normal loading $q$ (mean pressure) is generally as shown in Fig. 3.

Table 6

| Parameters characterizing the mechanical properties of snow | Temp., °C | Density, g/cm³ | | | | | |
|---|---|---|---|---|---|---|---|
| | | 0.15 | 0.2 | 0.3 | 0.4 | 0.5 | 0.6 |
| Internal cohesion $c_0$, kg/cm² | | 0.04 | 0.05 | 0.5 | 0.7 | 0.9 | 1.9 |
| Coefficient of friction $\tan \phi_0$ | | 0.25 | 0.33 | 0.35 | 0.40 | 0.42 | 0.6 |
| Modulus of deformation $E$, kg/cm² | −5 | 2–3 | 4–6 | 10 | 15–20 | 40 | 75 |
| Load bearing capacity $q_s$, kg/cm² | | 0.2 | 1.0 | 1.7 | 4.0 | 12.0 | 35.0 |
| Internal cohesion $c_0$, kg/cm² | | 0.05 | 0.06 | 0.52 | 0.9 | 1.2 | 2.2 |
| Coefficient of friction $\tan \phi_0$ | −10 | — | 0.35 | 0.40 | 0.43 | 0.45 | 0.5 |
| Modulus of deformation $E$, kg/cm² | | — | 6–8 | 15 | 25–30 | 55 | 100 |
| Internal cohesion $c_0$, kg/cm² | | 0.06 | 0.09 | 0.8 | 1.05 | 2.7 | 4.7 |
| Coefficient of friction $\tan \phi_0$ | | — | 0.4 | 0.4 | 0.48 | 0.5 | 0.55 |
| Modulus of deformation $E$, kg/cm² | −20 | — | 10 | 20 | 40 | 80 | 130 |
| Load bearing capacity $q_s$, kg/cm² | | 0.3 | 2.01 | 2.55 | 5.6 | — | — |
| Coefficient of sliding friction, $\phi_{sl}$ | −4 | 0.1 | 0.085 | 0.07 | 0.055 | 0.025 | 0.015 |
| | −16 to −30 | 0.14 | 0.097 | 0.08 | 0.065 | 0.035 | 0.02 |
| | −1 to +2 | 0.18 | 0.11 | 0.09 | 0.075 | 0.045 | 0.028 |

For relatively small load, the soil consolidates and forms a dense elastic core below the plate. Under the action of the vertical static load, this core moves downwards, compacting the adjacent soil layer. Deformation of this nature is represented by the first intercept, which may be in the form of a straight line or may be slightly curved (concave upwards).

The second intercept represents both the compaction of the soil as well as its shear. In this stage of loading, the forces resisting compaction are greater than the forces resisting lateral shift of the soil. When the compacted core

10

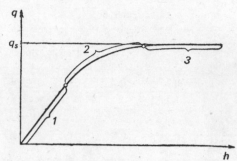

Fig. 3. Resistance of soil to indentation as a function of the depth of indentation
of the plate:
1–3—intercepts.

displaces downwards, the adjacent layers move aside due to shear deformation. As the load increases, the shear deformation increases, leading to a
progressive rise in the depth to which the plate sinks into the soil.

The third intercept is distinguished by an exclusively increasing shear
deformation. The resistance of the soil to lateral shear is completely overcome, and the plate rapidly sinks into the soil without any further increase
of load. This sudden sinking is accompanied by the soil being squeezed out
sideways from under the plate. The pressure $q_s$, at which the soil begins to
flow outwards, is known as its load bearing limit.

The relationship between the first and the second intercepts depends upon
the type and composition of the soils as also the size of the plate. For sandy
soils, the size of the first intercept is governed by the density of the soil. For
clayey soils (at low loads), the greater the moisture content the earlier the
shear deformation occurs.

The effect of the plate area on the above relationship is dual in nature.
On one hand, the larger the plate area, the greater the depth to which stresses
are propagated (Fig. 4) and, correspondingly, the greater its penetration due

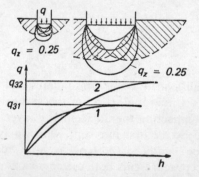

Fig. 4. The relationship $q=q$ ($h$) for various sizes of plates:
1—for a small size plate; 2—for a large size plate.

to compaction of the soil. On the other hand, the greater the width of the plate, the greater the soil resistance to shear. The latter may be schematically explained by the fact that the area of cross-section of the soil prism, subjected to shear under pressure $q_s$ (shown by broken lines in Fig. 4), is proportional to the square of the plate width. To confirm the above statement, Figs. 5 and 6 show experimental data [54] regarding the influence of the plate width on the zone of deformation spread along the depth of the soil $H'_s$ and on the horizontal deformation (shear).

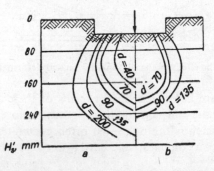

Fig. 5. The influence of the plate diameter on the soil deformation zone:
a—loose soil; b—settled soil.

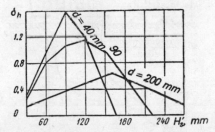

Fig. 6. The effect of the plate diameter on the relative lateral deformation
of the soil $\delta_h$.

Thus, when the width of the plate is increased, the deformation of the soil becomes greater in the zone of low loads, but in the zone of large loads, it exceeds the load bearing limit. As a consequence, the deformation reduces. The opposing influence of the plate width $b$ on the compaction and shear is due to the complex nature of the curve $h = h(b)$, which has a minimum (Fig. 7).

A plate corresponding to the minimum deformation of the soil must have a width which increases with an increase in the amount of sand particles in the soil; since for this condition, the influence of the plate width on the bearing capacity increases. The effect of the plate width on the bearing capacity is negligible for clay, and the curve $h = h(b)$ does not really have a minimum.

12

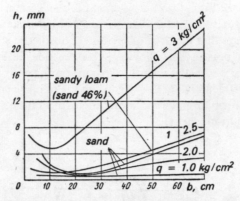

Fig. 7. The effect of the plate width on soil deformation *h* [69].

In soils which are heterogeneous in terms of their density, the effect of the plate width on the soil deformation becomes more complex. Consider two-layered soil, which is the one most often encountered. It consists of a soft upper layer over a comparatively hard lower layer (Fig. 8).

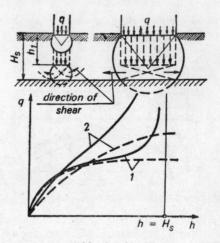

Fig. 8. The influence of a neighboring hard layer on soil deformation:

broken lines—deformation in the absence of a hard layer; full lines—in the presence of a neighboring hard layer; 1—for a small size plate; 2—for a large size plate.

The presence of a neighboring hard layer causes a unilateral effect on both types of deformations. The volume of compaction reduces, since there is a restriction to the depth to which deformation propagates. The shear reduces due to a reduction in the thrust. Likewise, the influence of the dimensions of the plate on soil deformation undergoes a change. As can be seen from Fig.

8, while loading with a small plate, the effect of the thickness of the soft layer $H_s$ becomes apparent only when the plate sinks to a considerable extent in the soil ($h > h_1$). However, for loading with a large plate, it begins immediately with the lowering of the plate.

Soils with a reverse combination of layers can also be found, consisting of a very firm upper layer overlying a weak one (very damp soil with a sod layer; extremely moist soils with a dry upper crust). For such soils, the bearing capacity of the upper layer is determined largely by the resistance of the soil to shear at the perimeter of the plate. The greater the diameter of the plate, the greater is the load carried per unit length of the perimeter. Hence in the above case, when the size of the plate is increased, the load bearing capacity decreases and the soil undergoes greater deformation.

## Mathematical Expression for Soil Deformation due to Normal Loads

The mathematical expression sought for the deformation of soils requires the following conditions to be satisfied: the expression should conform to the physical processes of soil deformation. Parameters characterizing the deformation of the soil are not dependent on the plate size. The expression should be capable of evaluating the deformation of the majority of the soils ordinarily used. It must contain parameters of soils in terms of which statistical data have been gathered. Finally, it must be suitable for practical applications.

The mathematical expression most extensively used for the deformation of soil as a function of loading is the Winkler-Gerstner-Bernstein formula

$$q = Ch^\mu, \tag{1}$$

where $C$ and $\mu$ are parameters of the soil.

Parameters $\mu$ and $C$ are assumed to be constant for a given soil. In actual practice, these parameters vary with the size of the plate (see Fig. 4). For practical purposes, this is the main difficulty faced in the use of the above expression.

In general, equation (1) cannot be used for expressing the soil deformation as a function of the load when the load, as well as the dimensions of the plate, vary over a wide range. It may be used for expressing function $q = q(h)$ only in certain specific cases for specific plate size and load ranges. Apart from this, it may be noted that parameters $\mu$ and $C$ do not have any physical meaning and are empirical constants.

In recent years, many attempts have been made to replace the power law by another more theoretically based or by a simpler expression for practical use. However, these expressions [like formula (1)] do not take into consideration the influence of plate size on soil deformation. Expressions for soil deformation which take into account the plate size are considered below.

Based on the experimental investigation of the deformation of soils, characteristic of agricultural lands, S.S. Saakyan [54] established a power law in which the absolute value of the vertical deformation of the soil takes the relative value

$$q = C\lambda_s^\mu, \tag{2}$$

where $\lambda_s = \dfrac{h}{b}$ ($b$ is the width of the plate) or $\lambda_s = \dfrac{h}{D'}$ ($D'$ is the diameter of the circle of area equivalent to the plate area).

The influence of plate size on the deformation of the soil is unilateral in formula (2). (It takes into consideration the fact that with an increase of plate size, deformation increases due to the stresses spreading to a greater depth, but does not account for the increase in bearing capacity and reduction in the relative portion of the deformation due to shear.) Hence, the proportionality between soil deformation and the plate diameter expressed by formula (2) may be applicable only over a restricted range of plate sizes (see Fig. 7).

M.G. Bekker [75], faced with the difficulties in using equation (1) for different sizes of plates, proposed the following variable power law,

$$q = \left( C_1 + \frac{C_2}{b} \right) h^\mu, \tag{3}$$

where $C_1$, $C_2$ and $\mu$ are constants for a given soil.

In contrast to the previous expression, equation (3) accounts for the influence of the plate size on the deformation of the soil with a variation for diverse types of soils due to the differences in the relationship between constants $C_1$ and $C_2$ and the different values of $\mu$. The ratio $C_1/C_2$ to some extent represents the type of soil and its composition; while the magnitude of $\mu$ reflects the nonhomogeneity of the soil. However, the nature of the influence of parameters $C_1$, $C_2$ and $\mu$ on function $h = h(b)$ is in agreement with the physical picture of deformation only over a certain range of values of $b$ and $\mu$. The function $h = h(b)$, according to equation (3), continuously increases for any parameters of the soil and hence, in general, does not correspond to the curve shown in Fig. 7. Results are unsatisfactory for large shear deformations (zone of small values of $b$) and the nonhomogeneous soils with an adjacent firm layer ($\mu > 1$).

Equation (3), just as equation (1), is purely empirical. Parameters $C_1$, $C_2$ and $\mu$ do not have any specific physical meaning.

V.F. Babkov proposed several expressions for evaluating soil deformation. Each one of these was suited for a specific range of soil conditions.

For soils in which shear deformation is predominant, he recommends the use of one of the formulas developed for determining the bearing capacity of soils:

$$q = S_b h + Q_b, \tag{4}$$

where

$$S_b = \frac{\gamma}{\tan^4\left(45° - \dfrac{\phi_0}{2}\right)};$$

$$Q_b = \frac{b\gamma \sin \phi_0}{4 \tan\left(45° - \dfrac{\phi_0}{2}\right) \sin^4\left(45° - \dfrac{\phi_0}{2}\right)}$$

$$+ \frac{c_0}{\tan\left(45° - \dfrac{\phi_0}{2}\right) \sin^2\left(45° - \dfrac{\phi_0}{2}\right)}.$$

Equation (4) includes soil parameters $\gamma$, $c_0$ and $\phi_0$, which are independent of the plate size and have a specific physical meaning. There is no doubt that this expression is preferable to the three previous formulas. However, equation (4) is only applicable to soils which yield. Deformation by compaction and the effect of the underlying firm soil layer is not taken into account by this equation.

For cases where a wheel deforms a small layer of compacted soil, Babkov [2] proposed the expression

$$h = \frac{t'q}{q + u'} \tag{5}$$

where $t'$ and $u'$ are parameters representing the properties of the soil.

Using equation (5), Babkov [2] and Ul'yanov [63] developed techniques for determining the depth of the tracks, based on a summation of the deformation of individual layers; the entire thickness of the soil being subdivided into such layers. These techniques ensure great accuracy. However, they are very complicated for the analyzation of the influence of the vehicle parameters on mobility.

The physical process of the deformation of homogeneous soil is very well-represented by a logarithmic expression obtained by G.I. Pokrovskii, based on the contact theory

$$h = \frac{b}{C} \ln \frac{(q + q_0)\, q_s}{(q_s - q)\, q_0} \tag{6}$$

where $q_0$ is the pressure corresponding to the initial density of the soil, kg/cm².

Equation (6) has a theoretical base. For homogeneous soil, it reflects the effect of the plate width on the increase in the region over which deformation spreads. If $q_s$ is replaced by $q$ from equation (4), then the influence of the plate width on the bearing capacity would be taken into account

16

$$h = \frac{b}{C} \ln \frac{(q+q_0)(S_bh+Q_b)}{q_0(S_bh+Q_b-q)}.$$  (7)

In order to evaluate the deformability of nonhomogeneous soils, particularly the widely prevalent soils having a firm sublayer, equation (7) needs extensive modification and even without this, the equation is still complicated enough for practical applications.

### Methods for Estimating Soil Deformability: Plate Size Effect

It was explained earlier that the action of a loaded plate causes two types of deformations: compaction of the soil particles and shear.

The expression for the relative lowering of the plate due to soil compaction may be assumed to be linear,

$$\lambda_s = \frac{\sigma}{E},$$  (8)

where $E$ is the modulus of soil deformation in the absence of shear, kg/cm².

In order to determine the absolute deformation due to compaction, it is necessary to know the law relating to the propagation of stresses in the soil along its depth and the thickness of the deforming soil layer.

Let us express the propagation of stresses in the soil by the equation

$$\sigma = \frac{q}{1+\left(\dfrac{z}{aD'}\right)^2},$$  (9)

where $z$ is the distance from the unit layer under consideration to the surface of contact between the plate and the soil, cm.

Equation (9) is corroborated by experimental data [63] (Fig. 9). The method for determining soil deformation in the absence of shear is shown in Fig. 10.

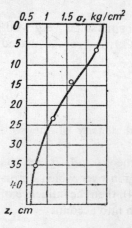

Fig. 9. Stress distribution in soil (curve drawn according to equation (9) for $q=2.4$ kg/cm²; $aD'=22.5$ cm [63]).

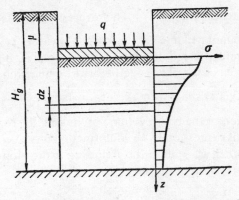

Fig. 10. Diagram for determining soil compaction.

Vertical compression of the unit layer from its initial thickness $dz_0$ may be expressed in terms of the relative deformation

$$dh = \lambda_s dz_0.$$

The thickness of the unit layer under a deformed condition is

$$dz = dz_0 (1 - \lambda_s).$$

The simultaneous solution of the last two expressions with equation (8) results in

$$dh = \frac{\sigma\, dz}{E - \sigma}. \tag{10}$$

It may be assumed that $E - \sigma \approx E$ in view of the small magnitude of $\sigma$ compared to $E$ ($\sigma \leqslant q_s$ and $q_s/E = 0.0125{-}0.003$).

Substituting the value of $\sigma$ obtained from equation (9), in equation (10) we have

$$dh = \frac{q\,dz}{E\left[1 + \left(\dfrac{z}{aD'}\right)^2\right]}. \tag{11}$$

After integrating this expression between the limits $z = 0$ to $z = (H_s - h)$, the expression for soil deformation is obtained as

$$h_d = \frac{qaD'}{E}\, \tan^{-1}\left(\frac{H_s - h}{aD'}\right). \tag{12}$$

The relative portion of the deformation due to shear increases progressively with the increase in load. The increase in total deformation due to soil shear is taken into consideration in equation (6) by multiplying the deformation due to compaction with $\dfrac{q_s}{q_s-q}$. This expression is used to estimate the deformation of a unit volume of the soil. However, from the above described physical nature of soil deformation (by a plate), it follows that shear leads to the lowering of the plate together with compaction of the soil's core.

Hence, it is highly advisable to make use of factor $\dfrac{q_s}{q_s-q}$ to estimate the relative deformation of the entire volume of the soil due to shear.

Multiplying this expression by the deformation due to compaction obtained from equation (12), we obtain the following expression relating the load and the total deformation of the soil:

$$q=\frac{1}{\dfrac{1}{q_s}+\dfrac{aD'}{Eh}\tan^{-1}\dfrac{H_s-h}{aD'}}. \tag{13}$$

The bearing capacity of the soil $q_s$ is not a soil constant but depends upon the plate dimensions. A large number of expressions have been proposed in soil mechanics for determining the bearing capacity of a soil. Results obtained from the different formulas differ only slightly [62]. The bearing capacity of a homogeneous soil is given by

$$q_{s0}=X_1b+X_2+X_3h. \tag{14}$$

For a strip plate [62]

$$X_1=\frac{\gamma\,(1-\text{Sh}^4)}{2\text{Sh}^5}; \qquad X_2=2c_0\,\frac{\text{Sh}^2+1}{\text{Sh}^3};$$

$$X_3=\frac{\gamma}{\text{Sh}^2}; \qquad \text{Sh}=\tan\left(45°-\frac{\phi_0}{2}\right).$$

The influence of the adjacent layer of firm soil is not taken into account in equation (14). When the plate approaches the hard bed of the soil, the bearing capacity increases progressively and approaches the bearing capacity of the underlying hard bed. The dependence of the bearing capacity upon the thickness of the deforming soil layer may be approximated by the expression

$$q_s=\frac{\pi q_{s0}}{2\tan^{-1}\dfrac{\pi\,(H_s-h)}{2aD'}}, \tag{15}$$

which is consistent with the physical nature of soil deformation.

In the case of soils which have a comparatively thin firm layer overlying a weak base, the loss in bearing capacity is due to a rupture of the upper layer. For such soils, the expression for $q_s$ may be assumed to be [28]:

$$q_s=A'+B'\,\frac{S_p}{F}, \tag{16}$$

where $S_p$ is the perimeter of the plate;

    $B'$ is a soil parameter characterizing the strength of the upper layer against rupture, kg/cm²;

    $A'$ is a soil parameter characterizing its compressive strength, kg/cm².

For small values of $A'$

$$q_s = c_0\, H_t\, \frac{S_p}{F},$$

where $H_t$ is the thickness of the turf layer, cm.

### The Effect of Plate Shape on Soil Deformation

The shape of the contacting surface of all types of modern high mobility tires with the soil is almost oval and, hence, it shall be estimated by the ratio of length $l$ to the contact width $b$.

K. Terzaghi [61] uses a coefficient $I$ to estimate the effect of the $\dfrac{l}{b}$ ratio on soil deformation due to compaction. Since diameter $D'$ appears in equation (12), we shall assume $I = 1$ for $\dfrac{l}{b} = 1$, in which case, the function $I = I\left(\dfrac{l}{b}\right)$ may be expressed as

$$I = \frac{0.03 + \dfrac{l}{b}}{0.6 + 0.43\,\dfrac{l}{b}}. \tag{17}$$

The expression for soil deformation due to its compaction then becomes

$$h_d = \frac{abqI}{E}\, \tan^{-1} \frac{H_s - h}{ab}.$$

The portion of deformation due to shear is characterized by the expression $\dfrac{q_s}{q_s - q}$. Consequently, one must consider the effect of the $(l/b)$ ratio on the bearing capacity $q_s$. In soil mechanics [61], the same type of equations are used for rectangular $\left(\dfrac{l}{b} = \infty\right)$, square and circular $\left(\dfrac{l}{b} = 1\right)$ plates but with different coefficients:

for rectangular plates

$$q_{s0} = X_1 b + X_2 + X_3 h;$$

for square plates:

$$q_{s0} = 0.8 X_1 b + 1.3 X_2 + X_3 h;$$

and for circular plates

$$q_{s0} = 0.6X_1b + 1.3X_2 + X_3h.$$

These equations may be combined by introducing suitable coefficients to account for the plate shape.

When $\left(\dfrac{l}{b} \approx 1\right)$, the contact between a tire and the soil has a shape midway between circular and rectangular. For $\dfrac{l}{b} = 1$, assuming some intermediate value for the coefficient of the first term (0.7), we may obtain an expression which is suitable for any $\dfrac{l}{b}$ ratio

$$q_{s0} = I_1X_1b + I_2X_2 + X_3, \tag{18}$$

where

$$I_1 = \frac{l}{l + 0.4b}; \qquad I_2 = \frac{l+b}{l+0.5b}.$$

Substituting the bearing capacity of the soil from equations (15) and (16) and the coefficients accounting for the shape of the line of contact from equations (17) and (18) in equation (13), we may obtain an expression for estimating the deformability of the soil. This will take into consideration the effect of both the dimensions of the contacting surface and its shape.

for marshy soils,

$$q = \frac{1}{\dfrac{F}{c_0 \, H_t \, S_p} + \dfrac{abI}{Eh} \tan^{-1} \dfrac{H_s - h}{ab}}; \tag{19}$$

for all other soils,

$$q = \frac{1}{\dfrac{2 \tan^{-1} \dfrac{\pi (H_s - h)}{2b}}{\pi (I_1X_1b + I_2X_2 + X_3h)} + \dfrac{Iab}{Eh} \tan^{-1} \dfrac{(H_s - h)}{ab}}. \tag{20}$$

The nature of the correlation described by equation (20) is shown in Fig. 11.

Equations (19) and (20) may be simplified for the solution of real problems in the following cases:

1. In the absence of an adjacent layer of hard soil

$$H_s = \infty, \ \tan^{-1} \frac{H_s - h}{ab} = \frac{\pi}{2}.$$

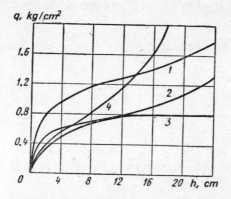

Fig. 11. Nature of correlation given by equation (20):

1—$E=20$ kg/cm²; $X_1=0.0267$ kg/cm³; $X_2=0.155$ kg/cm²; $H_8=50$ cm. 2—$E=5$ kg/cm²; $X_1=0.0065$ kg/cm³; $X_2=0.35$ kg/cm²; $H_8=40$ cm; 3—$E=15$ kg/cm²; $X_1=0.0002$ kg/cm³; $X_2=0.83$ kg/cm²; $H_8=200$ cm; 4—$E=15$ kg/cm²; $X_1=0.0023$ kg/cm³; $X_2=0.31$ kg/cm²; $H_8=25$ cm ($J=J_1=J_2=a=1$).

Writing $\dfrac{2E}{\pi a}=E_1$ (soil parameter), we have

$$q=\frac{E_1 h q_{s0}}{E_1 h + b q_{s0}}. \tag{21}$$

For clayey soils, the value of $q_{s0}$ is practically independent of $b$ and $h$ ($X_1\approx0$, $X_3\approx0$) and, hence,

$$q=\frac{E_1 h X_2 I_2}{E_1 h + b X_2 I_2}. \tag{22}$$

2. For soils with a thin layer of weak soil (a soil surface occurring immediately after rain or covered with a thin layer of snow and filled-in soils)

$$\tan^{-1}\frac{H_s-h}{ab}\approx\frac{H_s-h}{ab};$$

$$\frac{1}{q_s}\approx0 \text{ and } q=\frac{Eh}{H_s-h}. \tag{23}$$

Equation (23) is analogous to equation (5).

3. For waterlogged soils which do not have a neighboring hard soil layer, deformation occurs mainly due to lateral shear. Deformation due to compaction is almost nonexistent. For such conditions, it may be assumed that $\dfrac{ab}{Eh}\approx0$, in which case

$$q=X_1 I_1 b + X_2 I_2 + X_3 h. \tag{24}$$

This equation is analogous to equation (4) and was obtained by V.F. Babkov for waterlogged soils.

4. For soils of high bearing capacity $\dfrac{1}{q_s} \ll \dfrac{ab}{Eh}$, and, hence, it may be assumed that $\dfrac{1}{q_s} = 0$, so that

$$q = \frac{EhI}{ab \, \tan^{-1} \dfrac{H_s - h}{ab}}. \tag{25}$$

The last expression is characteristic for cohesive soils with a loose topsoil layer.

5. For homogeneous and highly compact soils, since $\dfrac{1}{q_s} = 0$ and $\tan^{-1} \dfrac{H_s - h}{ab} = \dfrac{\pi}{2}$, we have a simple linear relationship

$$q = \frac{Eh}{abI}. \tag{26}$$

## RESISTANCE OF SOIL TO SHEAR LOAD

### The Physical Nature of Soil Deformation due to Plate Displacement

Apart from the vertical load, if a horizontal force is applied (Fig. 12) to a plate, then the soil deforms in the direction of the applied force. It is often observed that an additional vertical deformation appears.

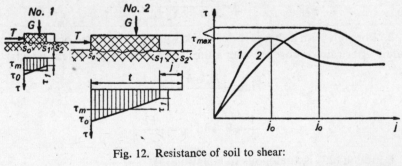

Fig. 12. Resistance of soil to shear:

1—plate No. 1; 2—plate No. 2.

At the instant when displacement commences (at very small values of the tractive force $T$), the soil particles attached to the surface of the plate, through which the force is transmitted, undergo displacement. As force $T$ increases, the zone of deformation propagation widens with a consequent increase in plate displacement.

When a particular value of $T$ is reached, the soil shears along the line $s_0 - s_1$ for lower down.

The resistance of the soil to shear is given by the expression

$$T_{max} = G \tan \phi_0 + c_0 b t'.$$

The value of $t'$ is less than $t$ and $s_0 \cdot s_1$, since mutual displacement of soil particles along line $s_0 - s_1$, does not occur at the same time. Initially these displacements occur close to point $s_0$ and with an increase of $T$, spread in the direction of $s_1$. The maximum value of $T$ corresponds to the instant when the internal adhesive forces act upon a large portion of the area $s_0 s_1$. With a further increase in displacement, the area of elementary segments, where the internal cohesion continues to exist between particles, are reduced. For this stage of displacement, the tractive force

$$T_s = G \tan \phi_0 + c_0' b (s_0 s_1),$$

where $c_0$ represents the internal cohesion which occurs when a layer of soil slides over the next one.

Dividing all the terms of the last two expressions by the plate area, we have

$$\tau_{max} = q \tan \phi_0 + c_0 \frac{t'}{t}; \qquad (27)$$

$$\tau_s = q \tan \phi_0 + c_0' \frac{s_0 s_1}{t}. \qquad (28)$$

Equation (27) differs from the well-known expression

$$\tau_{max} = q \tan \phi_0 + c_0, \qquad (29)$$

by the presence of the multiplying factor $\frac{t'}{t}$ with parameter $c_0$, which reflects the decrement in the area of shear due to horizontal compaction of the soil and the nonsimultaneity of the displacements occurring at the shearing plane.

The nature of the expression representing soil resistance to shear as a function of displacement $j$ differs significantly for various soils (Fig. 13). For granular soils, $c_0 = 0$ and, hence, the curve $\tau = \tau(j)$ does not have a maximum. The greater the internal cohesion (soil adhesion), the more pronounced is the maximum.

Values of $j_0$ and $\tau_{max}$ (see Fig. 12) depend upon the parameters of the plate: when $t$ is increased, the value of $j_0$ increases due to the increasing non-simultaneity of the displacements. The function $\tau_{max} = \tau_{max}(t)$ is extremely complicated. When $t$ increases, the nonsimultaneity of displacements becomes more severe, and the soil becomes more compact. The former leads to a reduction in the value of $\tau_{max}$, while the latter leads to its increase.

24

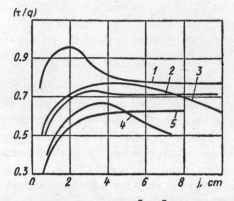

Fig. 13. Experimental dependence $\frac{\tau}{q}=\frac{\tau}{q}$ (j) for various soils:

1—loam (structure conserved), moisture $W=12\%$; 2—loam in a plastic condition, moisture $W=25\%$; 3—compacted soil, $q=0.95$ kg/cm² [3]; 4—compacted soil, $q=0.76$ kg/cm² [3]; 5—sand.

The influence of the second factor may be explained by an illustrative example. Let us compare two plates. No. 1 plate with a very small value of $t$ and No. 2 plate with a large value of $t$ for an identical value of $q$ (see Fig. 12). The effect of nonsimultaneity of displacements is not taken into consideration, since it is necessary to at least clarify the qualitative pattern of the process. We shall assume that the law of propagation of soil stresses is linear and that the relationship between resistance to shear and density is also linear. In such a case, for an identical value of $q$ near point $s_1$, soil shear for both plates occurs at the same value of $\tau_1$. As one moves further away from point $s_1$, compressive stresses increase and, correspondingly, the resistance to shear. It is obvious that for plate No. 2, the resistance to shear $\tau_0$ at the average shear stress $\tau_{av}$ at points $s_0$ is more for the area $s_0 s_1$ than that for plate No. 1.

Because of the opposing effects of the above two factors on $\tau_{max}$, its variation as a function of $t$ is insignificant. It is possible to obtain an optimal value of $t$ at which $\tau_{max}$ is the greatest.

Plate resistance to displacement relative to the soil depends not only on the parameters defining displacement of one layer of soil over another, but also on the friction between the cleats on the plate and the soil. Experiments show (Fig. 14) that the nature of relationship $\tau_r=\tau_r$ (j) for displacement of a rubber sheet on soil is similar to those shown in Figs. 12 and 13 for displacement of one soil layer over another. In such cases, it is not always necessary that sliding must occur at the plane of contact of the sheet with the soil. On several soils, for example on sands, adhesion between a rubber sheet and the soil is greater than between different layers of the soil.

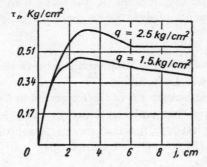

Fig. 14. The relationship between the resistance of a rubber sheet to displacement over a soil and the magnitude of the displacement (soil: loamy black soil with a loss of structural adhesion, moisture content—17%, area of displacement—100 cm²) [29].

Diverse values of adhesion in the zone of friction between the tire cleats and the soil as well as in the zone of soil shear further complicate the relationship between adhesion of the plate to the soil and the cleats. Figure 15 shows curves representing the dependence between the coefficient of adhesion and the pitch of the cleats on sandy soils at small normal loads ($q < 0.2$ kg/cm²). The curves show a distinctly clear maximum.

A significant change in the coefficient of adhesion with the pitch of the tire cleats occurs only at very small, practically unrealistic, loads ($q = 0.01$ to $0.02$ kg/cm²) for wheeled vehicles. When the load is increased, the influence of pitch on the adhesion coefficient markedly reduces and loses significance.

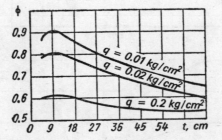

Fig. 15. Relationship between the adhesion coefficient and the pitch of cleats (on a tire) (soil–sand) [7].

The case considered above was a simplified one for the displacement of a plate relative to the soil. Real processes which occur during displacement of the soil are far more complicated and have not been sufficiently investigated so far. S.G. Vol'skii [10] observes the presence of self-excited processes during displacement of a plate over the soil. A study of self-excited processes would help explain the influence of dynamic factors on the adhesion properties of soils.

## Mathematical Expression for the Relationship between the Shear Resistance of Soil and its Deformation

The functional relationship $\tau = \tau(j)$ is expressed in several different forms, depending upon the problem under consideration and the degree of accuracy required. In the simplest case, function $\tau = \tau(j)$ is approximately represented by two straight lines (Fig. 16) given by equations

$$\tau = E'j \quad \text{for} \quad j \leqslant j_0; \tag{30}$$

$$\tau = q \tan \phi_0 + c_0 \quad \text{for} \quad j > j_0.$$

For most of the soils, this method appears to be a bit too rough. When one compares these linear equations (Fig. 16) with the experimental data given in Fig. 13, it is observed that the discrepancy is as much as 100% for cohesive soils.

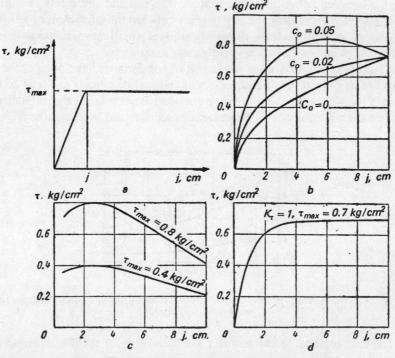

Fig. 16. Nature of expression $\tau = \tau(j)$:

a—according to equation (30); b—according to equation (31); c—according to equation (32); d—according to equation (33).

Function $\tau = \tau\,(j)$ is expressed by V.F. Babkov [2] as follows,

$$\tau = \left[ q \tan \phi_0 + c_0 \left( 1 - \frac{j}{t} \right) \right] \sqrt{j/j_0}. \tag{31}$$

The curves described by equation (31) are shown in Fig. 16b. These curves are close to the experimental for $j < j_0$. Here it must be emphasized that Babkov takes into account the reduction of internal cohesion in the soil, due to the decrease in the area over which these forces act when displacement is increased $\left[ \text{the term} \left( 1 - \frac{j}{t} \right) c_0 \right]$.

According to equation (31), the total internal cohesion decreases to zero at $j = t$. For $j > t$, the term $\left( 1 - \frac{j}{t} \right) c_0$ becomes negative, which is in contradiction to the physical meaning. It is obvious that $\left( 1 - \frac{j}{t} \right) c_0 \geqslant 0$. It may also be observed that, in fact, shearing of the soil (total loss of internal adhesion) occurs at $j < t$.

Parameter $j_0$ is not a constant for the soil but varies with the volume of soil displaced, particularly with $t$ as shown in the previous section.

The mathematical expression for function $\tau = \tau\;(j)$ was obtained by M. Bekker [75] by utilizing the equation used in the theory of vibrations:

$$\tau = \frac{c_0 + q \tan \phi_0}{Y_{\max}} \left[ e^{\left( -K_{\tau 2} + \sqrt{K_{\tau 2}^2 - 1} \right) K_{\tau 1} j} - e^{\left( -K_{\tau 2} - \sqrt{K_{\tau 2}^2 - 1} \right) K_{\tau 1} j} \right], \tag{32}$$

where $K_{\tau 1}$ and $K_{\tau 2}$ are parameters obtained from the curve fitting of experimental data;

$Y_{\max}$ is the maximum value of the expression in the square brackets.

The magnitude of parameters $K_{\tau 1}$ and $K_{\tau 2}$ varies with the size of the plate.

Equation (32) does not take into consideration the pitch $t$ of the cleats on a tire.

The nature of the curve described by equation (32) is governed by parameters $K_{\tau 1}$ and $K_{\tau 2}$ and is independent of $c_0$ and $\tan \phi_0$. This condition is in contradiction to the physical nature of the problem in the sense that the presence of a maximum is governed above all by the magnitude of the internal cohesion $c_0$ of the soil.

As can be seen from Fig. 16c, for large values of $j$, the magnitude of the specific resistance of the soil to shear $\tau$, obtained from equation (32), may be less than the internal frictional force ($q \tan \phi_0$), which once again contradicts the physical significance of the problem.

Many investigators abroad express the relationship $\tau = \tau\,(j)$ as an exponential function

$$\tau=(c_0+q \tan \phi_0)\left(1-e^{-\frac{|j|}{K'_\tau}}\right).$$

(33)

For most of the noncohesive soils, the experimental relationship $\tau= \tau(j)$ is close to exponential and, hence, for these, expression (33) is entirely acceptable. This equation is less suitable for cohesive soils for which $\tau=\tau(j)$ has a maximum. Apart from this, equation (33) does not take the pitch of the cleats on a tire into account.

The equation given below, proposed by V.V. Katsygin, is of considerable interest

$$\tau=f_s q\left(1+\frac{4f_f-3f_s}{2f_s \cos h -\dfrac{j}{K_\tau}}\right) \tan h \frac{j}{K_\tau},$$

(34)

where $f_s$ is the coefficient of sliding friction;

$f_f$ is the coefficient of static friction;

$K_\tau$ is a soil parameter.

This expression agrees well with experimental data. However, it is difficult to use since all three parameters $f_s$, $f_f$ and $K_\tau$, which express the properties of the soil, are not independent parameters of the soil (the magnitudes of $f_s$ and $f_f$ significantly vary with the load, while $K_\tau$ is dependent upon the pitch of the cleats on the tire). When equation (34) is transformed in terms of independent parameters, it becomes far more complicated.

None of the equations given above in their present form satisfy the conditions stated earlier, which must be satisfied by the expression for soil deformation. However, these formulas already have most of the initial information for obtaining the desired expression.

The nature of the rise of soil resistance to displacement with an increase of the latter is usually nonlinear. The curve $\tau=\tau(j)$ over the portion $j=0$ to $j_0$ is convex relative to the axis of $j$.

This may be suitably expressed by an exponential expression

$$\tau=\tau_m\left(1-e^{-\frac{|j|}{K'_\tau}}\right),$$

(35)

where $K'_\tau$ is a parameter (expressed in cm) which characterizes the deformability of soil due to displacement.

This equation is suitable for any value of $j$. It is useful for determining the value of $\tau$ for noncohesive soils for which the curve $\tau=\tau(j)$ does not have a maximum. If one substitutes $\tau_m$ in the above expression by

$$\tau_m=[q \tan \phi_0+c'_0+(c_0-c'_0)\,\zeta],$$

where $\zeta=1-\dfrac{m'j}{t}$ for $\dfrac{j}{t}<K'$ and $\zeta=0$ for $\dfrac{j}{t}>K'$ ($m'$ is a coefficient which takes into account the nonsimultaneity of displacements and $K' = \frac{j_m}{t}$ is a coefficient for soil shear), then one obtains an expression which describes a curve having a maximum. Thus, by combining terms from equations (31) and (33) and introducing certain corrections, one obtains an expression which satisfies the desired conditions, i.e., it becomes suitable for investigating the interaction between diverse types of vehicles and different types of soils.

Instead of using an exponential function to describe the relationship $\tau = \tau(j)$, one may use a hyperbolic function analogous to the expression used to describe the resistance of soil to indentation.

Analogous to the vertical deformation of the soil considered earlier, one may identify a linear deformation due to displacement $j_l$. This is characterized by the modulus of deformation due to shear $E'$ and a coefficient of the increase of deformation, which depends upon the relationship between the existing tangential stresses and the limiting value of displacement stresses.

In such a case, $j = j_l v_j$ where $j_l = \frac{\tau t}{E'}$; $v_j = \frac{\tau_m}{\tau_m - \tau}$; or

$$\tau = \frac{1}{\dfrac{1}{\tau_m} + \dfrac{t}{E' |j|}}. \tag{36}$$

Equation (36), just as equation (35), satisfies all the desired requirements. The coefficient of resistance to displacement $E'$ appears in it as the deformation parameter.

Thus, strictly speaking, it is necessary to have four independent soil parameters $c_0$, $c_0'$, $\phi_0$ and $E'$ to evaluate its properties. However, in most cases one may omit $c_0'$. Then the value of $\tau_m$ in equations (35) and (36) would be governed by the expression

$$\tau_m = q \tan \phi_0 + c_0 \zeta. \tag{37}$$

Figure 17 shows theoretical curves described by equations (35) and (36). The nature of the curves described is similar. However, for small values of $j$, the function $\tau = \tau(j)$ is more accurately described by equation (35). The final selection of a particular formula further depends on its suitability for mathematical transformations.

In order to determine the maximum value of resistance to displacement $\tau_{max}$ and its corresponding value of displacement $j_0$, let us equate the first derivative $\frac{d\tau}{dj}$ obtained from equation (36) to zero:

$$\frac{d\tau}{dj} = \frac{\left(\tau'_m - \dfrac{2c_0}{t} j\right)\left[\dfrac{(E' - c_0)}{t} j + \tau_m\right] - \dfrac{j}{t}\left(\tau'_m - \dfrac{c_0}{t} j\right)(E' - c_0)}{\left[(E' - c_0)\dfrac{j}{t} + \tau'_m\right]^2} = 0,$$

where $\tau'_m = q \tan \phi + c_0$.

Assuming $E' - c_0 \approx E'$ and solving the resulting expression, we have

$$j_0 = \frac{\tau'_m t}{E'}\left(\frac{\sqrt{E'}}{c_0} - 1\right). \tag{38}$$

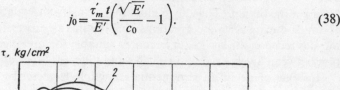

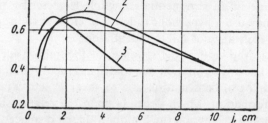

Fig. 17. Nature of the function $\tau = \tau (j)$ for $q = 1$; $\tan \phi_0 = 0.4$ and $c_0 = 0.5$:

1—according to equation (35) for $K'_\tau = 1$, $t = 10$ cm; 2—according to equation (36) for $E' = 20$, $t = 10$ cm; 3—according to equation (36) for $E' = 20$, $t = 5$ cm.

The expression for resistance to displacement $\tau_{max}$ may be obtained by substituting the value of $j_0$ in equation (36):

$$\tau_{max} = \frac{\tau'_m \left(\sqrt{E'} - \sqrt{c_0}\right)^2}{E' - c_0}. \tag{39}$$

Proceeding similarly with equation (35), we have

$$\frac{d\tau}{dj} = -\frac{c_0}{t} + \frac{\tau_m}{K'_\tau} e^{-\frac{j_0}{K'_\tau}} - \frac{c_0}{K'_\tau t} j_0 e^{-\frac{j_0}{K'_\tau}} + \frac{c_0}{t} e^{-\frac{j_0}{K'_\tau}};$$

$$i_0 = K'_\tau \ln\left(\frac{\tau_m t}{K'_\tau c_0} + 1 - \frac{j_0}{K'_\tau}\right). \tag{40}$$

It may be observed that the magnitude of displacement $j_0$, obtained by using equation (35), is expressed by a complex function which presents considerable difficulties during calculations. The expression for maximum resistance to displacement $\tau_{max}$ is even more complicated. Consequently, the computation of function $\tau = \tau (j)$ as also determination of the value of $j_0$ and $\tau_{max}$ becomes simpler when equation (36) and its first derivatives (38) and (39) are used. However the accuracy is somewhat improved when equation (35) is used.

# CHAPTER 2

# Wheel–Soil Interaction

## PHYSICAL PROCESSES OCCURRING WHEN A WHEEL ROLLS OVER SOIL

A wheel rolling over the soil has a different mechanical effect on the soil than that on soil compacted by a plate as described earlier.

The motion of a rigid wheel may be considered as the process of continuous rotation of a plate of a complex shape around a changing instantaneous center of rotation. During this action, the direction and velocity of the displacement of the elementary segments of the plate vary over different parts of the plate.

Experiments show that when the elementary segments of plate displacement are inclined away from the normal to the surface, soil resistance to compaction reduces. Hence, the resistance of soil to compaction, during the rolling motion of a wheel, must be less than that during the translatory motion of a plate.

The mechanics of soil deformation during the rolling of a wheel were investigated by M.Kh. Pigulevskii, A.K. Birulya [5], V.F. Babkov [2], S.S. Saakyan [54] and others. According to their findings soil deformation by a wheel may be subdivided into three types:

vertical displacement of soil (primarily due to compaction);

lateral displacement of soil towards the sides; and

displacement of soil in the direction of motion.

In the case of soils which may be closely packed, a compaction wedge is first formed below the wheel as in the case of a plate. When the loose soil layer is thin, as in the case of plowed soil, the compaction wedge can transform into the usual compression of a loose soil layer overlying a firm base. The lateral compaction of soil during the motion of an automobile wheel over loose soils appears to be weak, while over cohesive soils in a weak plastic and fluid state, it appears to be predominant. During one rotation of the wheel, the soil does not deform to the extent required by the corresponding load. Hence, there is a gradual increase in both the compaction wedge as well as in the lateral movement of the soil during successive passes of the wheel over a single track.

The third type of deformation, i.e. displacement of soil in the direction of motion, is governed by the kinematics of wheel rotation. This type of deformation is absent during the sinking of a plate and, consequently, is one of the principal distinctive properties of a rolling wheel.

Experiments show [2] that forward displacement of the soil is characteristic for all types of conditions of wheel movement (including that of a driving wheel, for which the total horizontal force is directed backwards). It has been observed that while the soil is displaced in the direction of motion, the soil undergoes both compression as well as shear. The relationship between these two types of deformation depends upon the state of the soil, the kinematics of rolling, and the width and speed of the wheel. The greater the speed, the lesser the time available for the forward displacement of soil. Correspondingly, the compaction is lighter. When it is impossible to compact the soil, it is forced upwards and to the sides. Increasing the width of the wheel makes it difficult for the soil to be driven to the sides. As a result, there is an increase in both the compaction of the soil ahead of the wheel and the height of the ridge which is formed in front of the wheel.

In order to make a detailed study of the special features of interaction between the soil and the rolling wheel, let us examine the graph of the normal loads at the point of contact between the wheel and the soil (Fig. 18) and compare it with the corresponding graph obtained for sinkage of a plate into the soil. The nature of the curve for transverse forces for a rigid wheel is similar to that of a plate, which attests to the similarity in the nature of the process of soil deformation under a plate and from a rolling wheel.

The pressure distribution in the longitudinal direction for a wheel differs significantly from that for a plate. At the rear portion of contact, the depth of the track is practically constant, while the normal loads vary from maxi-

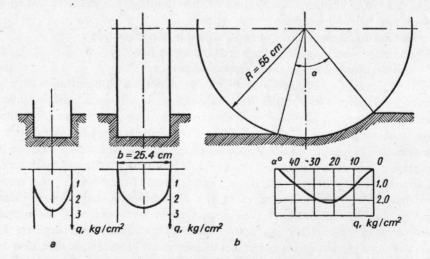

Fig. 18. Pressure distribution at the points of contact between (a) a plate and sand and (b) a rigid wheel and sand.

mum to zero. A fall in the normal load, while approaching the point at which contact is broken, may be attributed to the soil displacement. The domed shape of the normal load distribution curve for a plate is also due to ground shear. An increase in the cohesiveness and compressibility of the soil reduces displacement, and the normal load distribution in the latter portion of contact almost becomes rectangular in shape. On the other hand, when cohesiveness reduces the normal load, the distribution curve is close to triangular. To illustrate this, Fig. 19 shows the normal pressure distribution curves obtained on sand and loam.

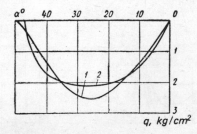

Fig. 19. Pressure distribution along the line of contact:

1—on sand; 2—on loam.

In the front portion of the zone of contact, there is a gradual increase in both the depth to which the wheel sinks in the soil and the normal loads. However, even here, function $q = q(h)$ differs from the analogous function obtained for the lowering of a plate. In that case, the load considered is the average value $q = \dfrac{G}{F}$. In the present case, the loads considered are the actual pressures acting on the front portion of the contact zone. Soil displacements affect the nature of these pressure distributions. At the points where contact is established, pressures reduce due to ground shear; while they increase towards the central portion of the contact zone (Fig. 19). The greater the tendency of the soil to shear, the more significant is the difference between functions $q = q(h)$ for a wheel and $q_m = q_m(h)$ for a plate.

## SPECIAL FEATURES OF PNEUMATIC WHEEL–SOIL INTERACTION

The deformation of a tire significantly complicates the process of interaction between the wheel and the soil, since it leads to a change in the shape of the contact surface and the nature of the contact pressure distribution.

The shape of the contact surface of an automobile tire and soil was first investigated by A.L. Marshak [37]. According to his data, during the rolling of a wheel, the leading portion of the contact surface in the longitudinal

34

section is close to the arc of a circle. The radius of this circle is greater than that of the undeformed tire, while its center is displaced in a forward direction, relative to the axis of the wheel.

Investigations, conducted by the author, of tire–soil interaction with a uniform tire pressure showed that the conclusions drawn by A.L. Marshak are valid only for comparatively rigid tires.

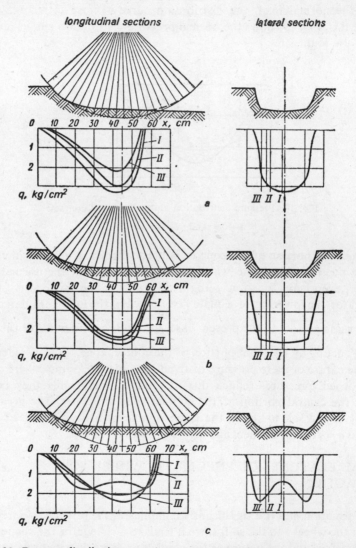

Fig. 20. Pressure distribution over the contact surface between a tire and soil (tire 12.00–18; $G_k = 1500$ kg; sandy soil, $\gamma = 1.3$ g/cm$^3$):

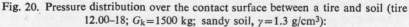

a—$p_w = 2$ kg/cm$^2$; b—$p_w = 1$ kg/cm$^2$; c—$p_w = 0.5$ kg/cm$^2$. I, II and III are sections.

Figure 20 demonstrates the longitudinal and lateral cross-sections of the contact surface between tire and soil and the contact pressure distribution for three different radial deformations of a tire. For small values of the radial deformation of a tire, the contact curvature in the longitudinal sections gradually reduces from a maximum value at the front portion to zero at the rear part of the contact surface. The curvature of contact over the lateral sections at the tire treads also reduces from the front to the rear of the contact surface. When the radial deformation of a tire increases to some specific value, a flat zone appears over the central part of the contact surface, which, in turn, increases with an increase in the radial deformation of the tire. For very large values of radial deformations (more than 25% of the height of the profile), the contact surface at the central portion takes a negative curvature, first over the transverse cross sections and later over the longitudinal ones.

The nature of pressure distribution over the contact surface is determined by the shape of the surface and the properties of the soil. For small radial deformations of the tire, when the flat portion of the contact zone is either nonexistent or is small, pressure distribution, both in the longitudinal and lateral sections, take on a parabolic form as in the case of a rigid wheel. With an increase in the deformation of the tire, the dome-shaped peak of the curve gets more and more truncated. The pressure distribution profiles in the longitudinal and lateral sections approach the trapezoidal with a gradually increasing upper base. With a further increase in deformation, when the central portion of the contact zone develops a negative curvature, the pressure distribution curve likewise assumes a concave shape in the central portion.

In the absence of a negative curvature, maximum pressures occur in the central part of the contact zone; while in the presence of a negative curvature, maximum pressures occur at the boundaries of this zone.

A change in the shape of the contact surface naturally affects the deformation of the soil. The larger the flat zone of contact, the smaller the tendency of the soil to shear and the smaller the corresponding lowering of the tire into the soil. The soil displacements towards the sides are even smaller when the contact zone has a negative curvature. Here one observes the "arch effect," which increases the load bearing capacity of the soil.

### The Relationship between the Depth of the Track and Contact Pressure between Wheel and Soil

What pressures at the points of contact between wheel and soil determine the depth of the track: maximum, average or something else? To answer this question, let us examine the experimental relationship obtained for the depth of the track as a function of the maximum pressures, the average pressures for the entire contact zone, the average pressures for the flat portion of the contact surface and the average pressures for the transverse section where these pressures are the greatest. Let us compare these with the expressions obtained for a plane plate (Fig. 21).

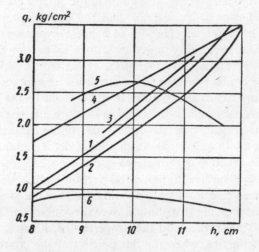

**Fig. 21.** Relationship between the depth of the track and pressures:

1—average pressure for a plane plate ($D=180$ mm); 2—average pressure for the flat portion of the tire-soil contact zone; 3—average pressure over the width of the tread; 4—maximum pressure at the central circular section; 5—maximum pressure at the sidewall circular sections; 6—average pressures for the entire contact surface (zone).

The average pressures for the entire contact surface (see curve 6 in Fig. 21) change very little for an increase or decrease of the internal tire pressure and the corresponding change in the depth of the track. This parameter cannot, therefore, be the decisive factor for determining the track depth. One also does not detect any strong relationship between the maximum pressures and the track depth. A well-defined relationship for track depth is characteristic for average pressures over the flat zone of contact and average pressures for the most severely loaded transverse section. These relationships may be utilized for determining the track depth. They differ slightly from the corresponding expressions for a plane plate. These differences could be taken into account by introducing correction factors for the shape of the contact surface and the loading conditions in equation (20).

### Influence of the Rolling Conditions of a Wheel on Soil Deformation

The rolling conditions of a wheel are governed by the load applied at its axis as well as its speed. In general, the load $P$ applied at the axis of the wheel (Fig. 22) is directed at some angle to the surface. Angle $\beta_0$, which gives the inclination of force $P$ to the normal one drawn from the plane of rotation of the wheel, is governed by the relationship between the thrust or tractive force $T$ and force $G_w$ normal to the rolling surface.

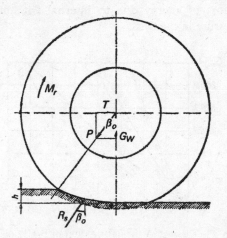

Fig. 22. Diagram of forces opposing the motion of a wheel:
$M_r$—retarding moment; $R_s$—reaction of the soil.

Many investigators feel that the track depth depends only on the normal force. In fact, it is not so. If the resistance of soil to compaction did not depend on the direction of the force, then the track depth would have been determined by the expression

$$h = [h(p)] \cos \beta_0.$$

In case of a linear deformation characteristic for soil ($h = K_p \cos \beta_0$, where $K$ is a coefficient), the track depth would not have been dependent on force $T$ since $p = \dfrac{G_w}{\cos \beta_0}$ and $h = KG_w$.

In reality, when the inclination of the applied force with respect to the normal force reduces, the shear resistance of the soil to compaction also reduces. Hence, on soft soils an increase in the thrust or tractive force always leads to an increase in the track depth. An increase in the speed of the wheel, as a rule, leads to a decrease in soil deformation due to the shorter time available for the force to act and the increase in the rate of loading. Because of the decrease in time duration, the soil does not deform to the fullest extent. When the rate of loading is intensified, the firmness of the soil is enhanced.

### Tire Deformability

Figure 23 shows curves representing the relationship between the radial deformation of a tire $\delta$, on a hard surface due to load $G_w$, for various tire pressures $p_w$. It may be noticed that these relationships differ from the linear. The maximum curvature is seen to occur in the initial stage of loading. The loading and unloading curves form a hysteresis loop; the area of which, representing the loss of energy due to internal friction, increases with a decrease of air pressure in the tires.

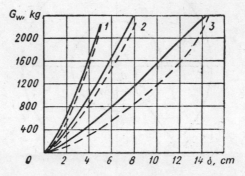

Fig. 23. Characteristic deformation of tire 12.00–18:

$1 — p_w = 3$ kg/cm$^2$; $2 — p_w = 1.5$ kg/cm$^2$; $3 — p_w = 0.5$ kg/cm$^2$.

For most of the tires, the curvature of the treads in the lateral cross sections is considerably smaller than that of their carcasses. For such tires, one may separately examine the deformation of the treadband (tire-tread zone) and the sidewalls. It is clear from Fig. 24 that at small loads, the major part of the deformation is of the treadband $\delta_t$ (laid out over a plane). At first, the deformation of the sidewall $\delta_s$ rises rapidly but later becomes linear with an increase of load.

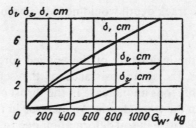

Fig. 24. Deformation characteristics of sidewall $\delta_s$ and tread $\delta_t$ of a four-ply tire 14.00–18.

The width and length of the contact surface, which increase with the deformation of the width of the tire profile, are governed by the radial deformation of the tires and are almost independent of the way in which radial deformation increases (increase of load or fall in tire pressure). Figure 25 illustrates these relationships for tires with adjustable tire pressure. For comparison, the same figure shows the chord lengths in the circumferential and meridional directions (broken lines). According to Fig. 25, the length of the contact may be expressed as the chord along with a coefficient varying from 0.8 to 0.9. The greater the rigidity of the tire carcass, the smaller is the magnitude of this coefficient.

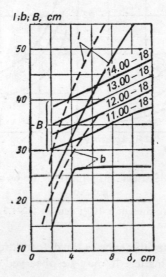

Fig. 25. Variation of profile width $B$, contact length $l$ and width $b$ as a function of radial deformation of tire (curves $l$ and $b_w$ for tire 12.00–18).

The contact width differs significantly from the corresponding chord. The maximum contact width equals the width of the treadband when it is laid out on a plane surface. The width of the tire profile varies almost linearly with radial deformation.

The contact width for tires interacting with soft soils is greater than that with hard surfaces. Because of this, the zone of the tire subject to deformation increases, but at the same time, the pressure and deformation at the central portion of the contact zone decrease. The softer the soil, the smaller is the deformation of the tire. With the increase of elasticity of a tire, the relative difference in its deformation on soft and hard surfaces reduces (Fig. 26). To explain this, let us arbitrarily subdivide the contact surface between tire and soil into a plane and a curvilinear zone. Let us assume that, for identical deformations of the tire on soil and a hard road surface, the area of the plane contact surface (on the soil) equals the contact area between a tire and a hard road. The deeper the groove, the greater is the relative portion of the curvilinear zone and a major part of the load is transmitted through this zone. For this condition, the load transmitted through the plane contact zone is smaller and so is the corresponding deformation of the tire.

When tires are more elastic, their deformation is greater, and the flat zone of contact correspondingly increases. In such cases, the curvilinear zone of

40

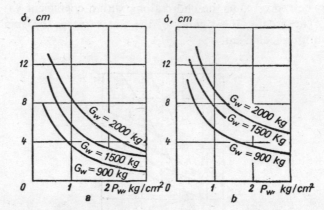

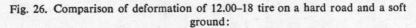

Fig. 26. Comparison of deformation of 12.00–18 tire on a hard road and a soft ground:

a—sandy soil, moisture content 8–10%; density 1.2–1.3 g/cm³; b—asphalt.

contact reduces so that the difference in the deformation of tires over soft and hard surfaces becomes smaller. It may be observed from Fig. 26 that for 12.00–18 tires, the radial deformation on moist sand is less than on a hard surface by 300%, for $G_w = 900$ kg and $p_w = 3$ kg/cm²; while it is only 10% for $G_w = 2000$ kg and $p_w = 0.5$ kg/cm².

Even when the radial deformation of a tire on a hard and soft surface is identical, the shape of the deformation profile is somewhat different. On soft soils, the deformation of the sidewalls is slightly greater than on a hard surface. However, it has been shown from experiments that this difference may be ignored.

**Tire-Soil Adhesion**

The force of adhesion between a tire and the ground is made up of the frictional force between the tire (rubber) and the soil $\Sigma \tau_r$ as well as the resistance to the shear of the soil enclosed between cleats $\Sigma \tau$. Both these forces depend upon the pressure and the magnitude of shear (see Fig. 14). The displacement of the tire elements relative to the ground may be taken as a measure of the readiness of the mutually interacting elastic bodies to the transmission of a tangential force.

In contrast to the displacement of a flat plate over the soil, the relative displacement at different points of contact is different for a wheel rolling over the ground. It was earlier established that even the pressure distribution over the contact surface is not uniform. Hence, the tangential forces at the different points of contact must be different in conformity with the magnitudes of displacement and pressure.

Figure 27 shows the distribution of tangential forces obtained for a rigid wheel rolling over a sandy soil. In the driven mode ($M_w = 0$), the tangential reactions of the soil over the front portion of the contact zone are directed ahead; while over the rear part of the contact zone, they are directed backwards and the summation of all the tangential forces is close to zero. In the present case, the thrust applied at the axis of the wheel equals the sum of the horizontal components of the normal reactions of the soil. In accordance with the characteristic nature of tangential pressure distribution, the displacement of wheel elements relative to the ground must be in the opposite direction at the front and rear portions of the contact zone.

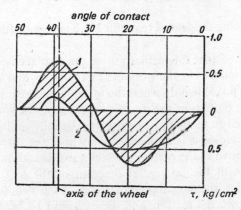

Fig. 27. Tangential force distribution obtained for the rolling of a rigid wheel over sand:

($R = 55$ cm, $G_w = 1550$ kg); 1—$R_w = 80$ cm, $h = 12$ cm; 2—$R_w = 55$ cm; $h = 10$ cm.

This type of displacement is in agreement with the concept of the rolling of a rigid wheel as a process of the turning of a wheel relative to an instantaneous center (Fig. 28). When the wheel turns over, relative to the instantaneous center of rotation $O$, the displacement vectors* of the wheel elements at the contact points do not coincide with the normal to the wheel surface. This gives rise to the tangential displacement of the wheel elements relative to the ground with the corresponding tangential forces. The inclination of the displacement vector from the normal is different at the different points of contact. It may be observed from Fig. 28 that over the front portion of the contact zone, the displacement vector at point $M_2$ is inclined in a backward direction from the normal, resulting in a forward tangential reaction of the ground. At the rear portion of the contact zone, during the driven mode for the wheel, the displacement vector for point $M_1$ is inclined ahead of the normal

---

*The concept of vectors has been introduced to obtain a simplified explanation of the complex process of the rolling of a wheel on soft ground.

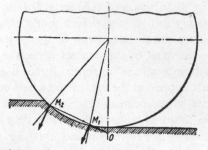

Fig. 28. Tangential forces appearing during the rolling of a rigid wheel.

with the corresponding tangential reaction of the ground directed backward at this point.

It may be observed that the inclination of the displacement vectors in an opposite direction, relative to the normals at the front and rear portions of the contact zone, is possible only when the instantaneous center of rotation $O$ is located below the bottom of the rut. Consequently, the rolling radius of a rigid wheel in the driven mode must be greater than the radius of the wheel.

When a turning moment is applied at the wheel, the displacement of the wheel elements, relative to the earth in a backward direction, increase with a consequent increase in the tangential reaction of the soil in the forward direction. During this, the instantaneous center of the rotation of the wheel is displaced in an upward direction, and the path covered by the wheel during one revolution reduces.

For a freewheeling mode ($T=0$, $M_w>0$), the sum of the horizontal components of the tangential forces equals the sum of the horizontal components of the normal reaction forces. In such a case, the backward displacements of the wheel elements are greater than those for the driven mode and, correspondingly, the rolling radius of the wheel reduces. A further increase in the turning moment leads to greater soil displacement and the skidding of the wheel.

Figure 29 shows the distribution of tangential forces at the points of contact between a pneumatic wheel and a hard flat surface. The nature of this pressure distribution is similar to that obtained for a rigid wheel on a soft ground.

The explanation of the kinematics of a rolling wheel in terms of its rotation about an instantaneous center is also applicable for the integration between an elastic wheel and a hard surface (Fig. 30).

If one considers the rolling of a pneumatic wheel as rotation about an instantaneous center $O$, then the displacement vectors are inclined away from the corresponding radial directions along which the elements of the tire must deform. As a result, the tire elements undergo tangential displacement relative to the rim as well as relative to the road.

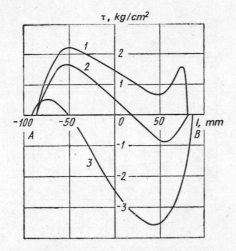

Fig. 29. Distribution of tangential forces at the contact between tire and road surfaces for different conditions:

1—driving mode; 2—driven mode; 3—braking mode (A—initiation of contact; B—termination of contact).

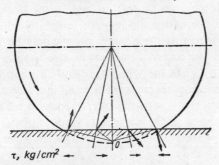

Fig. 30. Appearance of tangential forces during the rolling of an elastic wheel.

The magnitudes of tangential forces at the contact between tire and road are governed by the value of tangential deformation as well as the tangential rigidity of the tire. They are also limited by the forces of adhesion between the tire elements and the road. The latter depend on the adhesion coefficient and the tire pressure. If the force caused by the tangential deformation of the tire happens to be more than the adhesive force between the tire and the road, then the tires begin to skid.

Figure 31 shows the magnitude of skidding at the contact between a tire and a hard road for 13.00–18 and 6.00–16 tires. These graphs show that at small values of turning moment applied at the wheel, there is practically no skidding over the principal contact zone (not including the zones of initiation and termination of contact).

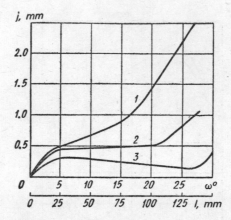

Fig. 31. Skidding of tire elements relative to the road:

1—$M_w$=190 kg·m, tire type 13.00–18, $p_w$=2.5 kg/cm², 2—$M_w$=17 kg·m, tire type 6.00–16, $G_w$=860 kg, $p_w$=2.2 kg/cm²; 3—$M_w$=25 kg·m; tire type 6.00–16, $p_w$=2.2 kg/cm², $G_w$=460 kg [42].

When an elastic wheel rolls on soft ground in the driven mode, the tires undergo tangential deformation along with tangential displacement of the soil. The tangential forces at the contact points may be expressed both in terms of tangential deformation of the tires as also in terms of tangential displacement of the soil. When the wheel transmits a continuously increasing moment, the tangential displacements of the soil increase at a far greater rate than the tangential deformation of the tire. Hence, it may be assumed that the tangential deformation of the tire is independent of the movement transmitted and is only governed by the shape of the tire over the contact zone. Under such conditions, the tangential forces may be better expressed in terms of the tangential displacement of the soil which is determined by the shape of contact and the radius of the rolling of the wheel.

### Energy Expenditure for the Rolling of a Wheel

During the rolling of an elastic wheel on soil, the power supplied at the wheel is expended in doing useful work (traction) as well as on deformation of the soil, the tires, slippage of the tires relative to the soil and in preventing the soil from sticking to the tire surface.

Resistance to rolling, caused by the loss of power in soil deformation, depends upon the size of the rut formed by the wheels, the resistance characteristics of the soil to compaction $q = q(h)$ and the extent to which soil is displaced forward. The forward displacement of the soil is significant in those cases where the angle of penetration (angle between the displacement vector of the tire elements and the normal) is greater than the angle of internal friction of the soil. In such cases, the soil is raked up by the wheel (bulldozer action), and the rolling resistance sharply increases.

The effect of velocity on the resistance of the soil to rolling occurs through two forces which are in opposition. When the velocity increases, the depth of the rut increases, which, as a consequence, must lead to a decrease in rolling resistance. At the same time, soil resistance may increase due to the forward displacement of the soil, which causes the rolling resistance to increase. Hence, the dependence of rolling resistance on velocity obtained by various investigators is found to differ significantly.

Resistance to rolling caused by power expended on the internal friction of the tire is governed by its deformation, wall thickness and the hysteresis properties of the materials from which the tire is made. The hysteresis properties of rubber vary with temperature due to which the tire losses slightly reduce when the temperature rises.

The nature of losses in a tire as a function of velocity are shown in Fig. 32. These losses become significant only at high speeds ($v > 50$ km/h), when the tire is unable to regain its shape at the contact zone and fluctuating deformations of the tire appear beyond the limits of the contact zone [43].

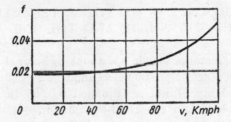

Fig. 32. Effect of speed on the rolling resistance of a wheel on a hard road (tire type 7.50–16; $G_w = 720$ kg; $p_w = 1.5$ kg/cm$^2$).

It was earlier established that tangential displacements of the tire relative to the soil or soil with respect to the soil occur under all types of conditions, including the driven and the free wheeling modes. Consequently, a part of the power delivered to the wheel is always expended on friction when the wheel slips. The power lost during slippage is governed by the magnitudes of frictional forces and tangential displacements, which depend upon the location of the instantaneous center of the rotation of the wheel as well as on the curvature and length of the contact surface. It is extremely difficult to obtain these from experiments separately.

Hence, for the rolling of a wheel without slippage, they are usually clubbed together with losses due to soil deformation; for rolling with slippage, they are included in the losses due to speed of the wheel.

The power lost in overcoming adhesion of the soil to the tire becomes significant for black soils (chernozem) and loess-like soils as also for loamy soils with a moisture content close to $w_0 = 0.5$–$0.6$. The stickiness of the soil impedes the rolling of a wheel, as the tire leaves the zone of contact when it tears itself away from the soil. Resistance to rolling due to the stickiness of the soil is proportional to the width of the contact zone and the specific force resisting the stripping of a rubber sheet from the soil. Apart from this, the sticky nature of the soil increases the adhesive force at the points of contact. As a result, there is an increase in the power lost on partial skidding and slippage.

The most significant disadvantage caused by soil stickiness is the clogging of the space between the treads, which sometimes covers the entire running portion of the tire. This leads to a significant increase in resistance to rolling as well as a fall in adhesion.

Even today one of the most complex and unresolved problems is that of providing self-cleaning treads for tires running over sticky soils. The self-cleaning ability of tires may be enhanced by choosing a rational shape for the treads, providing a substantial change in the curvature of the running surface of the tire at the point of exit from the zone of contact and by use of surface films which discourage the soil from sticking to the tire.

## ANALYTICAL TREATMENT OF THE INTERACTION BETWEEN AN ELASTIC WHEEL AND THE SOIL

Following are the assumptions made while making an analytical examination of the interaction between an elastic wheel and soil.

1. The deformability of soil is estimated by equation (13), while the adhesive properties of soil are expressed by equation (36).

2. Deformation of tire and soil at any arbitrary cross-section during contact is governed by the average pressure at this section over the width of the tread and over the width of contact.

3. While evaluating the resistance of the soil to deformation, the influence of the direction of the forces acting on the ground and the bearing capacity of the soil are taken into consideration.

4. The average tangential forces over the width of contact are governed by the adhesive properties of the soil as also by the magnitudes of pressure and displacements of tire elements relative to the soil.

5. The rolling speed of the wheel is not considered in the first stage of analysis. The influence of speed on the process of interaction between wheel and soil is considered below.

The schematic diagram of the wheel–soil interaction is shown in Fig. 33. Let us constitute equations for the components of the forces in the directions of the $x$ and $z$ axes and an equation for the moments relative to the axis of the wheel:

$$\int\limits_{x_2}^{x_1} b\,(q\cos\alpha_w + \tau\sin\alpha_w)\,\frac{dx}{\cos\alpha_w} = \int\limits_{x_2}^{x_1} b\,(q + \tau\tan\alpha_w)\,dx = G_w; \tag{41}$$

$$\int\limits_{x_2}^{x_1} b\,(\tau - q\tan\alpha_w)\,dx = T; \tag{42}$$

$$\int\limits_{x_2}^{x_1} b\,[(q + \tau\tan\alpha_w)\,x + (\tau - q\tan\alpha_w)\,(\xi + z)]\,dx = M_w, \tag{43}$$

where $b$ is the width of contact, cm;

$q$ and $\tau$ are the average normal and tangential reactions of the soil over the contact width, $kg/cm^2$;

$\xi$ is the distance from the wheel axis to the surface of the soil, cm;

$z$ is the depth of submergence of the tire in the soil, cm.

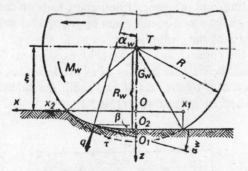

Fig. 33. Schematic diagram for wheel-soil interaction during the rolling of a wheel.

To solve the above equations, it is first necessary to find an analytical relationship between the deformation of the tire, the surface of contact between tire and soil and the distribution of normal pressures and tangential forces over the contact surface.

**Deformation of the Tire Profile**

The shape of the lateral cross-section at the contact surface is determined by the nature of deformation of the tire profile under the action of an external load.

Under equilibrium conditions, the shape of the profile depends upon the dimensions of the rim (width $B_F$ and diameter $d$), the length of the tire-cord fibers and the angle $\beta'_c$ subtended by them.

The radius of curvature at any point on the profile may be expressed in terms of the expression developed by V.L. Biderman [4]:

$$\rho = R \frac{(1-\lambda_0^2)\cos\beta_c' \sqrt{1-\lambda^2\sin^2\beta_c'}}{\lambda\,[2-(3\lambda^2-\lambda_0^2)\sin^2\beta_c']},$$

where $\lambda_0 = \dfrac{r_0}{R}$ ($r_0$ is the radius at the widest part of the tire and $R$ is the outer radius of the tire);

$\beta_c'$ is the angle subtended by the tire-cords with the crown;

$$\lambda = \frac{r}{R},$$

where $r$ is the radius at any point on the profile.

A nomogram method was proposed by V.L. Biderman for the configuration of the tire profile for practical calculations.

The difference between the actual shape of the profile from the theoretical is explained by the unequal wall thickness of the carcass, the rigid attachment of the beading, and presence of lugs and treads on the treadband of the tire. Type $P$ tires have a non-equilibrium profile shape, depending upon the diameter and width of the girdle ring.

Considering the approximate nature of all expressions for the interaction between a tire and the soil, the profiles of all modern tires may be described with sufficient accuracy by the arcs of two radii: the sidewalls by the radius $r_s$ and the treadband by the radius $r_r$ (Fig. 34).

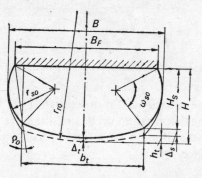

Fig. 34. Parameters of a tire profile.

The technical characteristics of a tire are often expressed in terms of the width of the profile $B$, the height of the profile $H$, the width of the rim $B_F$, the width of the tread $b_t$, the deflection of the tread $h_t$, and the thickness of the tread at the central portion $\Delta_t$ and at the shoulder $\Delta_s$.

The rest of the parameters of the tire profile in an undeformed condition shall be determined from the geometrical conditions shown in Fig. 34. The suffix 0 indicates the undeformed condition of the profile.

Sidewall parameters:

$$r_{s0} = \frac{H_s}{2 \cos p_0 \sin \dfrac{\alpha_{s0}}{2}}; \tag{44}$$

$$H_s = H - h_t - \Delta_s; \tag{45}$$

$$p_0 = \tan^{-1} \frac{B_F - b_t}{2 H_s}; \tag{46}$$

$$B_F - b_t = 2 r_{s0} \left[ 1 - \cos \left( \frac{\alpha_{s0}}{2} + p_0 \right) \right].$$

Solving the last expression simultaneously with equation (44), we obtain the expression for the angle $\alpha_{s0}$ and the arc length $l_{s0}$ of the sidewalls:

$$\alpha_{s0} = 2 \sin^{-1} \frac{H_s}{A^2 + (H_s \cos p_0)^2}$$

$$\times [A - \sqrt{A^2 - (1 - \cos^2 p_0) [(H_s \cos p_0)^2 + A^2]}; \tag{47}$$

$$l_{s0} = r_{s0} \alpha_{s0}, \tag{48}$$

where $A = (B - b_t) \cos p_0 - H_s \sin p_0$.

When

$$b_t = B_F; \quad p_0 = 0; \quad r_{s0} = \frac{H_s^2}{4 (B - B_F)};$$

$$\alpha_{s0} = 2 \sin^{-1} \frac{H_s}{2 r_{s0}}.$$

Tread parameters:

$$r_{t0} \approx \frac{b_t^2}{8 h_t}; \tag{49}$$

$$\alpha_{t0} = 2 \sin^{-1} \frac{b_t}{2 r_{t0}}; \tag{50}$$

$$l_{t0} = r_{t0} \alpha_{t0}, \tag{51}$$

where $l_{t0}$, $\alpha_{t0}$ are the arc length and angle of the tread.

Profile parameters:

$$U = l_{t0} + 2 l_{s0} + 2 \Delta_s. \tag{52}$$

When the tire deforms under load, the profile shape changes due to deformation of the sidewalls $\delta_s$, deflection of the tread $\delta_t$ and compression of the rubber tread $\delta_r$.

The radial deformation of the tire is

$$\delta = \delta_s + \delta_t + \delta_r. \tag{53}$$

### Deformation of the Sidewall

Let us write down the expression for the horizontal components of the forces acting on the sidewalls (Fig. 35):

$$p_w(H_s - \delta_s) - N\left[\sin\left(\frac{\alpha_s}{2} + \rho\right) + \sin\left(\frac{\alpha_s}{2} - \rho\right)\right] = 0,$$

where $N$ is the tensile force on the carcass in the meridional direction.

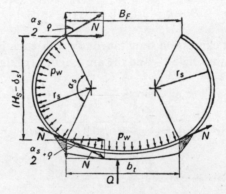

Fig. 35. Forces acting on the elements of a tire profile.

The sum of the horizontal components of the tensile forces acting on the sidewalls in the circumferential direction may be assumed to be zero in view of the small curvature of the sidewalls in this direction.

Let us write down the expression for the vertical components of the forces acting on the tread,

$$p_w b_t - Q - 2N\cos\left(\frac{\alpha_s}{2} + \rho\right) - 2N_1 = 0,$$

where $N_1$ is the vertical component of the force acting on the tread in the circumferential direction.

In the absence of an external load ($Q = 0$), from the last expression we obtain:

$$2N_{10} = p_w b_t - 2N\cos\left(\frac{\alpha_s}{2} + \rho\right).$$

When $Q \neq 0$ a flat zone of width $b'$ appears in the central portion of the contact zone. The vertical component of the circumferential force over this flat portion is zero. Bearing this in mind, for $Q \neq 0$, we have,

$$2N_1 = \left(1 - \frac{b'}{b_t}\right)\left[p_w b_t - 2N \cos\left(\frac{\alpha_s}{2} + \rho\right)\right].$$

Substituting $b' = \dfrac{Q}{p_w}$ in this expression and simultaneously solving the last four expressions, we obtain an equation for the load in terms of the deformation of the sidewalls,

$$Q = p_w b_l \left[1 - C_1\left(1 - \frac{\delta_s}{H_s}\right)\frac{\cos\left(\frac{\alpha_s}{2} + \rho\right)}{\sin\frac{\alpha_s}{2}\cos\rho}\right], \tag{54}$$

where

$$C_1 = \frac{\sin\frac{\alpha_{s0}}{2}\cos\rho_0}{\cos\left(\frac{\alpha_{s0}}{2} + \rho_0\right)}.$$

The angles $\alpha_s$ and $\rho$ change during the process of deformation. Utilizing the geometrical representation of the tire shown in Fig. 35, $\alpha_s$ and $\rho$ may be expressed in terms of $\delta_s$ as follows:

$$\rho = \tan^{-1}\frac{B_F - b_t}{2(H_s - \delta_s)}; \tag{55}$$

$$\sin\frac{\alpha_s}{2} = \frac{H_s - \delta_s}{2r_s \cos\rho};$$

$$l_s = \alpha_s r_s.$$

Expanding $\sin\dfrac{\alpha_s}{2}$ in the Fourier series and solving the last two expressions for $\alpha_s$, we have

$$\alpha_s = 2\sqrt{6\left(1 - \frac{H_s - \delta_s}{l_s \cos\rho}\right)}. \tag{56}$$

The rigidity of the tire walls, which increase the resistance of the tire to deformation and redistributes the pressure over the tread width, was not taken into consideration in the above derivation. Special investigations carried out by the author showed that it is possible to account for the effect of the rigidity of the tire walls on the deformation of the profile by replacing the parameter $p_w$ in equation (54) by $(p_w + k_t)$, where $k_t$ is the pressure exerted by the tire on the road when $p_w = 0$.

**Deformation of the Tread and Distribution of the Vertical Component of Pressure over the Width and Length of the Contact**

The nature of pressure distribution over the width of the contact zone is determined by the internal air pressure, rigidity of the carcass, design of the tread and deformation of the tire. Considering the exceptional complexity involved in obtaining an analytical solution to this problem, we turn to an approximate solution based on experimental results.

For a wheel rolling over a hard road surface (Fig. 36)

$$q_y = (p_w + k_t) - k_y \, y^n.$$

Since the total external load

$$Q = 2 \int_0^{b/2} \left[ (p_w + k_t) - k_y \, y^n \right] dy,$$

the coefficient

$$k_y = \frac{[(p_w + k_t) \, b - Q] \, (n+1)}{2 \left( \dfrac{b}{2} \right)^{(n+1)}}.$$

Substituting this expression in the equation for $q_y$, we have

$$q_y = (p_w + k_t) \left\{ 1 - (n+1) \, y^n \left[ \left( \frac{2}{b} \right)^n - \frac{Q}{2 \, (p_w + k_t)} \left( \frac{2}{b} \right)^{(n+1)} \right] \right\}. \qquad (57)$$

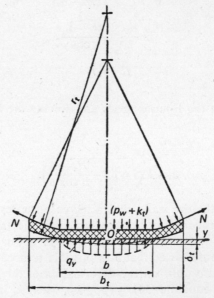

Fig. 36. Deformation of the tread on a hard surface.

For most tires, $n \approx 2$ and hence,

$$q_y = (p_w + k_t) \left\{ 1 - 3 \left( \frac{2y}{b} \right)^2 \left[ 1 - \frac{Q}{b(p_w + k_t)} \right] \right\}.$$

Assuming $q_y = 0$ and $y = \frac{b}{2}$ in equation (57), the expression for the width of the contact zone is obtained as

$$b = \frac{(n+1) Q}{n (p_w + k_t)}. \tag{58}$$

The maximum contact width is limited by the width of the tread $b \leqslant b_t$. If from equation (58), $b$ is found to be greater than $b_t$, then $b$ should be taken equal to $b_t$.

The deformation of the tread due to flexure may be determined by its deflection over the chord equal to the contact width, i.e.

$$\delta_t = \frac{b^2}{8r_t}. \tag{59}$$

Compression of the tread rubber may be expressed by equation

$$\delta_r = \frac{q_y \Delta_t}{m \psi F_r}, \tag{60}$$

where $\Delta_t$ is the thickness of the rubber tread;

$\psi$ is a coefficient for the increase in rigidity of the rubber, due to its resistance to deformation in the transverse direction.

When a wheel rolls over a soft soil, the contact width is often more than the width of the tread (Fig. 37). Tread deformation may occur, not because

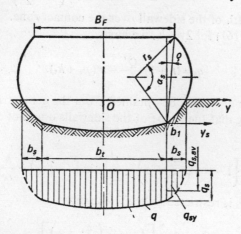

Fig. 37. Deformation of the tire profile over soft soil.

of spreading over the surface but due to the flexure over the entire width. Taking these features into account, the basic expression may be written as,

$$q_y = (p_w + k_t) \frac{b}{b_t} - k_y y^n.$$

Following the same procedure as in the previous case, we have

$$q_y = (p_w + k_t) \frac{b}{b_t} \left\{ 1 - (n+1) \left( \frac{2y}{b_t} \right)^n \left[ 1 - \frac{Q'}{b_t (p_w + k_t)} \right] \right\}, \tag{61}$$

where $Q'$ is the vertical reaction of the ground acting on the tread.

The value of $n$ depends upon the properties of the soil and the tire, while the values of $b$, $\delta_t$, $\delta_r$ and $\delta$ are obtained from equations (53) and (58) to (60) as in the previous case. In this case, one should substitute the coefficient $k_m$ in place of $m$ in equation (60). This allows for the pressure distribution between the cleats and the troughs between them. The coefficient

$$k_m = 1 - \frac{\Delta_t}{h} (1 - m),$$

where $h$ is the depth to which the tire sinks in the soil.

When $\frac{\Delta_t}{h} \geqslant 1$, $k_m = m$.

The vertical reaction of the soil acting on the sidewalls may be determined from the expression

$$q_{sy} = q_s \left[ 1 - \left( \frac{y_s}{b_s} \right)^2 \right], \tag{62}$$

where $q_s$ is the pressure at the edges of the tread $\left( y = \frac{b_t}{2} \right)$;

$b_s$ is the width of the sidewall over the contact zone.
From equation (61) for $2y = b_t$, we have

$$q_s = (n+1) \frac{Q'}{b_t} - n (p_w + k_t). \tag{63}$$

The magnitude of $b_s$ may be obtained from the geometrical relationships (Fig. 37), assuming that the shape of the sidewalls does not change under the reaction force $q_{sy}$:

$$b_s = r_s \left\{ 1 - \cos \left( \frac{\alpha_s}{2} + \rho \right) - \frac{1}{2} \left[ \sin \left( \frac{\alpha}{2} + \rho \right) - \frac{h}{r_s} \right]^2 \right\}. \tag{64}$$

The range of $b_s$ is restricted by the inequality

$$0 < b_s < r_s \left[ 1 - \cos \left( \frac{\alpha_s}{2} + \rho \right) \right].$$

The depth $h$, to which the tire element under consideration sinks in the soil, may be obtained with the help of equation (13) by replacing the diameter of the plate by the width of contact:

$$q = \frac{1}{\dfrac{1}{q_s} + \dfrac{ab_{con}}{Eh} \tan^{-1} \dfrac{H_s - h}{ab_{con}}},$$

where $b_{con} = b_t + \zeta_z b_s$; $\zeta_z = \dfrac{q_{s\,av}}{q_s}$ (Fig. 37);

$q = \dfrac{Q'}{b_t}$ is the mean pressure over the width of the tread.

The lugs on the tread as well as the recesses between them sink to different depths in the soil. Hence, when the height of the lugs is relatively large, the expression for $q$ may be transformed as follows:

$$q_1 = \frac{1}{\dfrac{1}{q_s} + \dfrac{ab_{con}}{Eh} \tan^{-1} \dfrac{H_s - h}{ab_{con}}};$$

$$q_2 = \frac{1}{\dfrac{1}{q_s} + \dfrac{ab_{con}}{E(h - \Delta_t)} \tan^{-1} \dfrac{H_s - h + \Delta_t}{ab_{con}}}; \tag{65}$$

$$q = mq_1 + (1 - m)\, q_2.$$

The sum of all the vertical reactions of the soil on the tire profile is

$$Q = Q' + \frac{4}{3}\, q_s b_s$$

or, substituting $q_s$ from equation (63) in the above expression, we have

$$Q = Q' + 4b_s \left[ \frac{Q'}{b_t} - \frac{2}{3} (p_w + k_t) \right]. \tag{66}$$

The change in the shape of the tire profile and the distribution of soil reaction over the contact width as a function of the radial deformation $\delta$ may be analyzed with the help of equations (53) to (66).

A solution for the generalized problem, which does not require a special analysis of each of the components contributing to the deformation of the tire ($\delta_s$, $\delta_t$ and $\delta_r$), may be obtained by using simplified expressions for the deformation of the tire profile instead of the equation system (53) to (60). The simplified expression may be obtained by applying the method of approximations to these equations:

$$Q' = 0.5\, (p_w + k_t)\, \delta C_t \left( 3.5 - \frac{\delta c_t}{b_t} \right), \tag{67}$$

where

$$c_t = \frac{B}{H} + 1.5 \frac{H}{B};$$

$$\alpha_s = 2 \sqrt{6 \left[ 1 - \frac{2(H-\delta)}{U-b_t} \right]}; \tag{68}$$

$$r_s = \frac{u-b_t}{2\alpha_s}. \tag{69}$$

The simplified expression for $b_s$ and $b_{con}$ may be obtained from equation (64), assuming $\rho = 0$:

$$b_s = r_s \left[ 1 - \cos \frac{\alpha_s}{2} - \frac{1}{2} \left( \sin \frac{\alpha_s}{2} - \frac{h}{r_s} \right)^2 \right]; \tag{70}$$

$$b_{con} = b_t + \frac{4}{3} b_s. \tag{71}$$

Pressure $q$, exerted at an arbitrary point of contact (see Fig. 33), is governed by the depth of sinkage of this point in the soil, its distance from the beginning or end of the contact zone (the smaller value is used), the ratio of length of width of the contact zone, the direction in which the elementary force $\sqrt{q^2 + \tau^2}$ acts and the characteristic angle $\beta$.

To solve the given problem, we shall start with equation (13), which expresses the normal reaction of the soil as a function of the depth of sinkage and width of contact.

The influence of the coordinate $x$ and the $\frac{l}{b}$ ratio shall be taken into account by making use of equations (17) and (18) for the coefficients $I$, $I_1$ and $I_2$.

Let us first consider the compacted soil (neglecting displacements). The average pressure is expressed at the contact through the depth of the plate sinkage and dimensions of the contact surface using equation (17):

$$q = \frac{E h_d' (0.6b + 0.43l)}{ab (0.03b + l)},$$

where

$$h_d' = \frac{h_d}{\tan^{-1} \dfrac{H_s - h_d}{ab}}.$$

Apart from this, average pressure may also be obtained from the pressure distribution diagram as,

$$q = \frac{1}{l} \int_0^l q_x \, dx,$$

where $q_x$ is the average pressure over a strip of the plate of $dx$ in length.

Solving the above two equations for $q_x$, we obtain the expression for pressure distribution over the length of contact of a plate during soil compaction:

$$q_x = \frac{Eh'_d}{ab} I_x, \qquad (72)$$

where

$$I_x = 0.43 + \left(\frac{0.18b}{0.03b + x}\right)^2;$$

$x$ being the distance at which the point lies from the beginning or end of the contact zone; and

$$x \leqslant l.$$

The effect of displacements on pressure distribution may be taken into account by obtaining an expression for $q_x$ when $q = q_s$.

As in the previous case,

$$q_s = \frac{1}{l} \int_0^l q_{sx}\, dx.$$

Solving the equation simultaneously with equation (18) for $q_{sx}$, we have

$$q_{sx} = I_{x1} X_1 b + I_{x2} X_2 + X_3 h, \qquad (73)$$

where

$$I_{x1} = \frac{x(x + 0.8b)}{(x + 0.4b)^2};$$

$$I_{x2} = 1 + \left(\frac{b}{2x + b}\right)^2.$$

Substituting the coefficients $I_x$, $I_{x1}$ and $I_{x2}$ in equation (20), we obtain the formula for pressure distribution over the length of the plate as follows,

$$q_x = \cfrac{1}{\cfrac{2\tan^{-1}\dfrac{\pi(H_s - h)}{2b}}{\pi(I_{x1} X_1 b + I_{x2} X_2 + X_3 h)} + \dfrac{ab}{EhI_x}\tan^{-1}\dfrac{H_s - h}{ab}}. \qquad (74)$$

Figure 38 shows the pressure distribution over the sole of a plate calculated according to equation (74):

for linear deformation of the compacting soil $\left(\dfrac{1}{q_s} = 0\right)$;

for noncohesive soils $(c_0 = 0)$;

for cohesive soils $(c_0 \neq 0, \phi_0 \neq 0)$.

58

These pressure distribution diagrams coincide with the data obtained by K. Terzaghi [61].

When the pressure distribution along the length of contact of an elastic tire with soil is considered, one must also take three other parameters into account. These are the shape of contact, which may not be flat, the elasticity of the tire and the direction in which the forces acting at the contact surface are inclined away from the vertical and normal to the contact surface.

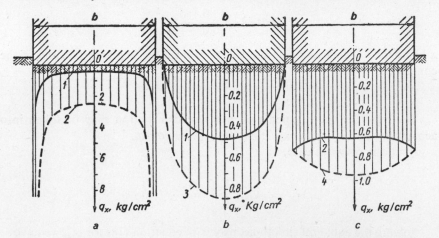

Fig. 38. Pressure distribution over the sole of a plate calculated from equation (74):

$b = 20$ cm; $a = 2$; $H_s = \infty$; a)— $\dfrac{1}{q_s} = 0$; $E = 50$ kg/cm²; b)—$X_1 = 0.04$; $X_2 = 0$; $X_3 = 0.01$; $E = 50$ kg/cm²; c)—$X_1 = 0.04$; $X_2 = 0.3$; $X_3 = 0$; $E = 30$ kg/cm²; 1—$h = 1$ cm; 2—$h = 5$ cm; 3—$h = 20$ cm; 4—$h = 25$ cm.

The three parameters enumerated above are interrelated. The shape of the contact surface depends upon the deformability of the tire. The direction in which the forces at the contact surface act depends on the shape of the latter.

The shape of the longitudinal section of the contact surface is characterized by the relationship $z = z(x)$ and may be taken into account in equation (74) by substituting $z$ in place of $h$.

As can be observed from the graphs shown in Fig. 20, the nature of pressure distribution corresponds to the shape of the contact surface. Hence, when the shape of the contact surface is taken into consideration, the effect of the elasticity of the tire is also included in it.

In this case, many of the contrasting factors connected with the different types of preliminary deformations of the soil, under rigid and elastic plates, remain unaccounted for even when in the final stage. The parameters at the contact surface between the soil and the plates are the same. However, these differences do not have any significant influence on the load bearing capacity and the final deformation of the soil. N.N. Maslov [38], during his analysis of the load bearing capacity of soils, observes that taking the rigidity of the plate into account does not show any great effect. According to the data of K. Terzaghi [61], the settlement of a flexible foundation differs very slightly (about 7.3%) from that of a rigid one.

## The Effect of Load Direction on Pressure Distribution

If the load is applied, not along the normal but at some angle to it, then the load bearing capacity and the thickness of the deformed soil layer change in the direction in which the forces act $\left[\text{instead of } (H_s - z) \text{ it will be } \dfrac{H_s - z}{\cos \beta}\right]$.

There is practically no acceptable solution for taking into account the effect of the direction of load on the bearing capacity of the soils. To account for this factor, as a first approximation, let us compare the expressions for the bearing capacity of the soil for vertical sinkage $q_s$ and horizontal displacement $q_h$ [61]:

$$q_h = \frac{1}{2}\, \gamma b \tan^2\left(45° + \frac{\phi_0}{2}\right) + 2c_0 \tan\left(45° + \frac{\phi_0}{2}\right); \qquad (75)$$

$$q_{s0} = \gamma b\, \frac{\left[1 - \tan^4\left(45° + \dfrac{\phi_0}{2}\right)^2\right]}{\tan^5\left(45° - \dfrac{\phi_0}{2}\right)} + 2c_0\, \frac{1 + \tan^2\left(45° + \dfrac{\phi_0}{2}\right)}{\tan^3\left(45° - \dfrac{\phi_0}{2}\right)}.$$

The structure of these expressions is identical and, hence, the expression for $q_h$ may be represented as

$$q_h = \phi_1' X_1 b + \phi_2' X_2, \qquad (76)$$

where $X_1$ and $X_2$ are unknown parameters of the bearing capacity [see equation (14)];

$$\phi_1' = \frac{\tan^2\left(45° + \dfrac{\phi_0}{2}\right) \tan^5\left(45° - \dfrac{\phi_0}{2}\right)}{2\left[1 - \tan^4\left(45° - \dfrac{\phi_0}{2}\right)\right]} \approx 0.08 \tan \phi_0;$$

$$\phi_2' = \frac{\tan\left(45° + \dfrac{\phi_0}{2}\right) \tan^3\left(45° - \dfrac{\phi_0}{2}\right)}{1 + \tan^2\left(45° - \dfrac{\phi_0}{2}\right)} \approx 0.5\text{--}0.01\, \phi_0.$$

The problem of determining the bearing capacity for any angle of inclination of the contact surface $\alpha_c$ was solved by Kögler for ideal sand [61] (Fig. 39):

$$q_{s\alpha} = \frac{\gamma b \sin^2 (\alpha_c - \phi_0)}{2 \sin \alpha_c \sin (\alpha_c + \delta') \left[1 - \sqrt{\dfrac{\sin (\phi_0 + \delta') \sin \phi_0}{\sin (\alpha_c + \delta') \sin \alpha_c}}\right]}, \tag{77}$$

where $\delta'$ is the angle between the normal to the contact surface and the direction of the resultant force $P$.

If $\alpha_c = \dfrac{\pi}{2}$ and $\delta' = 0$, then $q_{s\alpha} = \dfrac{\gamma b \cos^2 \phi_0}{2 (1 - \sin \phi_0)^2}$.

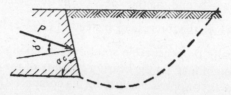

Fig. 39. Diagram representing soil resistance.

Comparing this expression with equation (75) for $c_0 = 0$, we have

$$\frac{\cos^2 \phi_0}{(1 - \sin \phi_0)^2} = \tan^2 \left(45° + \frac{\phi_0}{2}\right).$$

A comparison of equations (14) and (77) shows that for $\alpha_c = \pi$ and $\delta' = -\phi_0$, the discrepancy is small. Consequently for an ideal sand surface, the functional relationship $q_{s\alpha} = q_{s\alpha} (\alpha_c)$ may be expressed by equation (77), where

for $\alpha_c = \dfrac{\pi}{2}$; $\delta' = 0$,

and $\alpha_c = \pi$; $\delta' = -\phi_0$.

While investigating the wheel–soil interaction, it is essential to take into account the influence of the direction of the elementary force $\sqrt{q^2 + \tau^2}$ given by angle $\beta$ (see Fig. 33) on the bearing capacity. For this, the coefficients $K_{\beta 1}$ and $K_{\beta 2}$ are introduced into the bearing capacity equation (73) to take into account the direction in which the forces act:

$$q_{s0} = K_{\beta 1} I_{x1} X_1 b + K_{\beta 2} I_{x2} X_2 + X_3 z. \tag{78}$$

Since the curve $q_s = q_s (\alpha)$, obtained from equation (77), is close to hyperbolic and at $\beta = 0$, $K_{\beta 1} = K_{\beta 2} = 1$, the coefficients $K_{\beta 1}$ and $K_{\beta 2}$ may be expressed by the equations

$$K_{\beta 1} = \frac{C_1 - \beta}{C_1 + \beta}; \quad K_{\beta 2} = \frac{C_2 - \beta}{C_2 + \beta}.$$

The values of $C_1$ and $C_2$ may be obtained by putting $\beta = \dfrac{\pi}{2}$.

According to equation (76)

$K_{\beta 1} \approx 0.08 \tan \phi_0$; $K_{\beta 2} = 0.5 - 0.01 \, \phi_0$.

Substituting these values in the equations for $K_{\beta 1}$ and $K_{\beta 2}$, we have

$$C_1 = \frac{\pi}{2}\left(\frac{1+0.08 \cot \phi_0}{1-0.08 \cot \phi_0}\right) \approx \frac{\pi}{4 \tan \phi_0};$$

$$C_2 = \frac{\pi}{2}\left[\frac{1+(0.5-0.01 \, \phi_0)}{1-(0.5-0.01 \, \phi_0)}\right] \approx \frac{3}{2}\,\pi$$

and consequently,

$$K_{\beta 1} = \frac{\pi - 4 \tan \phi_0 \, \beta}{\pi + 4 \tan \phi_0 \, \beta}; \quad K_{\beta 2} = \frac{3\pi - 2\beta}{3\pi + 2\beta}. \tag{79}$$

When the direction in which the force is applied is taken into account, equation (74) becomes

$$q_x = \cfrac{1}{\cfrac{2 \tan^{-1} \cfrac{\pi (H_s - z)}{2b \cos \beta}}{\pi (K_{\beta 1} I_{x1} X_1 b + K_{\beta 2} I_{n2} X_2 + X_3 z)} + \cfrac{ab}{EzI_x} \tan^{-1} \cfrac{H_s - z}{ab \cos \beta}}, \tag{80}$$

where $K_{\beta 1}$, $K_{\beta 2}$, $I_x$, $I_{x1}$, $I_{x2}$ are determined from equations (79), (72) and (73).

## Mathematical Expression for the Shape of the Longitudinal Section of the Tire-Soil Contact Surface

At any arbitrary section $x$ (see Fig. 33), the deformations of the soil and tire are determined by the force $Q' = qb_t$. Apart from this, $\delta_x$ and $z$ are related by the geometrical relationship

$$\delta_x = h + \delta - z - \frac{x^2}{2R}.$$

Substituting this expression in place of $\delta$ in equation (67) and simultaneously solving equations (67) and (80), we have

$$\frac{(p_w + k_t)}{2b_t}\left\{3 - \left[1.75 - \left(\frac{B}{H} + 1.5 \, \frac{H}{B}\right)\left(h + \delta - z - \frac{x^2}{2R}\right)\right]^2\right\}$$

$$= \cfrac{1}{\cfrac{2 \tan^{-1} \cfrac{\pi (H_s - z)}{2b \cos \beta}}{\pi (K_{\beta 1} I_{x1} X_1 b + K_{\beta 2} I_{x2} X_2 + X_3 z)} + \cfrac{ab}{EzI_x} \tan^{-1} \cfrac{H_s - z}{ab \cos \beta}}. \tag{81}$$

Equation (81) relates the coordinates $x$ and $z$ with the tire parameters $H$, $B$, $R$, $b_t$, $p_w$ and $k_t$; soil parameters $X_1$, $X_2$, $X_3$, $E$, $H_s$ and $a$ and the parameters which characterize the tire-soil interaction $h$, $\delta$ and $\beta$. The angle $\beta$, representing the direction in which the elementary force acts at each point of contact, depends upon the rolling radius $R_w$ and is derived from geometrical relationships (see Fig. 33)

$$\beta = \tan^{-1} \frac{R_w - \xi - z}{x}. \tag{82}$$

The rolling process is considered to be the turning over of the line of contact relative to an instantaneous center $O$. The direction of the resultant elementary force at the point of contact is assumed to coincide with the displacement vector, but within the limits of the friction angle. If $(\beta - \alpha_c) > \phi_0$ (where $\alpha_c$ is the angle between the line of contact and the horizontal plane), then the force vector does not coincide with the displacement vector. Hence, while determining angle $\beta$, it is necessary to introduce the limits $|\beta - \alpha_c| \leqslant \phi_0$.

For this angle,

$$\alpha_c = \tan^{-1} \frac{dz}{dx}. \tag{83}$$

Considering the comparatively small effect $\alpha_c$ has on the results derived from equation (81), one may approximate $\alpha_c$ from the expression

$$\alpha_c = \frac{2hx}{x_2^2},$$

which is obtained on the assumption that the line $x_2 O_2$ represents the arc of an arbitrary circle of radius $R_{con} = \dfrac{x_2^2}{2h}$.

An analysis of the various factors influencing the shape of the longitudinal section of the contact surface shows that the decisive factors are the radius of the wheel, the depth of the ruts formed by the wheels and the radial deformation of the tires. In all cases, the radius of curvature continuously increases from the beginning to the end of the contact surface. In the vertical axial section $(x = 0)$ and at the rear portion of the contact surface $(x < 0)$, the radius of curvature of the longitudinal section is almost infinite.

Keeping this in view, one may obtain an extremely simple expression for the longitudinal line of contact

$$z = h - c' x^{n'},$$

where $c'$ and $n'$ are parameters determined by the initial conditions: at $z = 0$ and $x = x_2$, we have $h = c' x_2^{n'}$.

Apart from this, to ensure a smooth joining of the curves at the point $z = 0$, $x = x_2$ (see Fig. 33), the following condition must be satisfied,

$$\frac{dz}{dx} = -\frac{x_2}{\xi}.$$

Differentiating this equation for $z$ with respect to $h$ $\left[\text{and substituting}\right.$

$c' = \dfrac{h}{x_2^{n'}}\Big]$, we have

$$\frac{x_2^{n'+1}}{\xi} = hn'x^{n'-1}.$$

The expressions for the parameters $n'$ and $c'$ may be obtained from the above expression and that for $h$ as

$$n' = \frac{x_2^2}{h\xi}; \quad c' = \frac{h}{\dfrac{x_2^2}{x_2^{h\xi}}}.$$

Substituting these in the equation for $z$, the expression for the shape of the longitudinal section of the contact surface is obtained as

$$z = h\left[1 - \left(\frac{x}{x_2}\right)^{\frac{x_2^2}{h\xi}}\right], \tag{84}$$

where

$$x_2 = \sqrt{(2R - \delta - h)(\delta + h)}; \tag{85}$$

$$\xi = R - \delta - h. \tag{86}$$

At the rear of the contact surface $(x = 0 - x_1)\ z = h$

$$x_1 = \sqrt{(2R - \delta)\,\delta}. \tag{87}$$

## Distribution of the Tangential Soil Reaction along the Length of the Contact Surface

The tangential force at any point of contact may be expressed with the help of equations (36) and (37) by suitably transforming them as

$$\tau = \frac{m}{\dfrac{1}{q_1\,\phi_r} + \dfrac{t}{E_r\,j}} + \frac{1 - m}{\dfrac{1}{q_2\tan\phi_0 + c_0\zeta} + \dfrac{t}{E'j}}, \tag{88}$$

where $q_1$, $q_2$ and $\zeta$ are given by equations (65) and (35).

The schematic diagram shown in Fig. 40 is considered to determine $j$. When the tire rotates around the instantaneous center $O_1$, through angle $d\alpha$, point $A$ is displaced by $dS = O_1A\,d\alpha$. The tangential component of this displacement is

$$dj = dS\sin(\alpha - \beta) = O_1A\sin(\alpha - \beta)\,d\alpha.$$

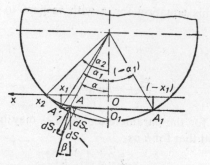

Fig. 40. Diagram for determining $j$.

Assuming that

$$O_1A = \frac{(\xi+z)\tan\alpha}{\cos\beta};$$

$$\tan\beta = \frac{R_w-(\xi+z)}{(\xi+z)\tan\alpha},$$

and rearranging

$$dj = \left[(\xi+z)\frac{1}{\cos\alpha} - R_w\cos\alpha\right]d\alpha; \qquad (89)$$

and

$$i = \int_{\alpha_2}^{\alpha}\left(\frac{\xi+z}{\cos\alpha} - R_w\cos\alpha\right)(-d\alpha).$$

The solution can be simplified by replacing the curve $x_2AA_1$ by the straight line $x_2A_1'A_1$.

For the intercept $x_2 A_1'$

$$\frac{\xi+z}{\cos\alpha} = R;$$

$$i_1 = R\,(\alpha_2-\alpha) - R_w\,(\sin\alpha_2-\sin\alpha). \qquad (90)$$

For the intercept $A_1'\,A_1$,

$$j = R\,(\alpha_2-\alpha_1) - R_w\,(\sin\alpha_2-\sin\alpha) + (\xi+h)\ln\frac{\tan\left(\dfrac{\pi}{4}+\dfrac{\alpha_1}{2}\right)}{\tan\left(\dfrac{\pi}{4}+\dfrac{\alpha}{2}\right)}. \qquad (91)$$

Expressing the value of $R_w$ in terms of the radius of the pure rolling of the wheel, characterized by the absence of skidding and spinning,

$$R_w = R_{w0}\,(1-\delta_s), \qquad (92)$$

where $R_{w0}$ is the radius of pure rolling.

When $\delta_s = 0$, $j = 0$ at the end of the contact zone.

For all modern tires, the value of $R$ changes over the width of the wheel

$$R_{av} \approx R - \frac{h_t}{3}.$$

Substituting the values of $R$ and $R_w$ in equation (91), the expression for the radius $R_{w0}$ of the entire tire

$$R_{w0} = \frac{\left(R - \dfrac{h_t}{3}\right)(\alpha_2 - \alpha_1) + (\xi + h)\ln \dfrac{\tan\left(\dfrac{\pi}{4} + \dfrac{\alpha_1}{2}\right)}{\tan\left(\dfrac{\pi}{4} - \dfrac{\alpha_1}{2}\right)}}{\sin\alpha_1 + \sin\alpha_2}. \tag{93}$$

The values of $\alpha_1$, $\alpha_2$ and $\sin\alpha_1$ may be expressed in terms of the deformations of the tire and soil as follows:

$$\alpha_1 = \cos^{-1}\left(1 - \frac{\delta'}{R'}\right);$$

$$\alpha_2 = \cos^{-1}\left(1 - \frac{\delta' + h}{R'}\right); \tag{94}$$

$$\sin\alpha_1 = \sqrt{\frac{\delta'}{R'}\left(2 - \frac{\delta'}{R'}\right)},$$

where $\delta' = \delta - \dfrac{h_t}{3}$; $R' = R - \dfrac{h_t}{3}$.

Equations (89) to (94) enable the determination of the tangential displacement of the soil at any point of contact as a function of the diameter of the wheel, slippage and tire and soil deformations.

For a hard road surface $h = 0$, $\alpha_2 = \alpha_1$,

$$R_{w0} = \frac{R - \delta}{2\sin\alpha}\ln \frac{\tan\left(\dfrac{\pi}{4} + \dfrac{\alpha_1}{2}\right)}{\tan\left(\dfrac{\pi}{4} - \dfrac{\alpha_1}{2}\right)}; \tag{95}$$

$$j = (R - \delta)\ln \frac{\tan\left(\dfrac{\pi}{4} + \dfrac{\alpha_1}{2}\right)}{\tan\left(\dfrac{\pi}{4} + \dfrac{\alpha}{2}\right)} - R_{w0}(1 - \delta_s)(\sin\alpha_1 - \sin\alpha). \tag{96}$$

## Rolling Resistance

The resistance of soil to rolling is determined from the equation

$$P_{fg} = \frac{M_w}{R_{w0}} - T, \tag{97}$$

where $T$, $M_w$ and $R_{w0}$ are obtained from equations (42), (43) and (93).

The losses due to tire deformation during rolling may be subdivided into two components:

i) losses due to internal friction within the walls of the tire during the course of their bending and returning to normal shape;

ii) losses due to internal friction in the rubber of the treads due to their cyclic compression.

Rolling resistance due to these components of the losses may be designated as $P_{ft1}$ and $P_{ft2}$.

The work expended on the deformation of an element of the tire (profile) may be expressed by the equation

$$dA = \int_0^\delta QR \, d\alpha \, dz',$$

where $Q$ is the load on the tire element under consideration;

$z'$ is the actual value of $\delta$.

The work expended on the bending of the tire walls (deformation of the profile) for one rotation of the wheel is given by,

$$A = R \int_0^\delta \int_0^{2\pi} Q dz' \, d\alpha = 2\pi R \int_0^\delta Q \, dz'.$$

This work is made up of the work done in compressing the air inside the tires and on overcoming the elasticity of the tire walls. The work done in compressing the air is completely reversible. Part of the work expended on overcoming the elasticity of the tire walls is lost in internal friction, which may be estimated by the hysteresis loss coefficient $\psi_1$.

The ratio of work done in overcoming tire-wall elasticity to the total work expended on the deformation of the profile can be expressed in terms of the ratio of the component of the pressure due to tire wall elasticity and the total pressure:

$$\frac{A_e}{A} = \frac{k_t}{p_w + k_t}.$$

Using the last two equations, we can obtain the expression for rolling resistance due to deformation of the tire walls:

$$P_{ft1} = \frac{A_e \psi_1}{2\pi R} = \frac{k_t \psi_1 b_t}{p_w + k_t} \int_0^\delta q \, dz'.$$

Expressing pressure $q$ in terms of $\delta$ and using equation (67) and condition $q = \dfrac{Q}{b_t}$, we have

$$q = \frac{(p_w + k_t)\,\delta c_t}{2b_t}\left(3.5 - \frac{\delta c_t}{b_t}\right).$$

Substituting the expression for pressure $q$ in the equation for $P_{ft1}$ and integrating, we have

$$P_{ft1} = \frac{\psi k_t c_t \delta^2}{2}\left(1.75 - \frac{\delta c_t}{3b_t}\right). \tag{98}$$

The losses due to internal friction in the rubber due to its cyclic compression are determined by the internal friction coefficient $\psi_2$, pressure $q$ and the thickness of the rubber.

Work done due to friction within the rubber of the tire treads can be expressed by the expression

$$A_r = \psi_2 s b_t \int_0^{\delta_r} q_z dz,$$

where $s$ is the path traversed by the treads.

Substituting the following in the expression for $A_r$

$$q_z = \frac{E_r z}{\Delta_t}; \quad \delta_r = \frac{q\Delta_t}{k_m E_r},$$

and integrating, we have

$$A_r = \frac{\psi_2\,s b_t\,\Delta_t\,q^2}{2 E_r\,k_m};$$

$$P_{ft2} = \frac{A_r}{s} = \frac{\psi_2\,b_t\,\Delta_t\,q^2}{2 E_r\,k_m}. \tag{99}$$

A summation of the components of the forces resisting rolling due to deformation losses in the tires gives

$$P_{ft} = P_{ft1} + P_{ft2} = \frac{\psi_1\,k_t\,c_t\,\delta^2}{2}\left(1.75 - \frac{\delta c_t}{3b_t}\right) + \frac{\psi_2\,b_t\,\Delta_t\,q^2}{2 E_r\,k_m}. \tag{100}$$

Rolling resistance due to soil adhering to the tires may be determined by the simple expression

$$P_{fa} = \left(b_t + 2b_s\right)\frac{x_1^2}{2R_{w0}}P_a, \tag{101}$$

where $P_a$ is the specific force resisting the detachment of a rubber sheet from the soil.

## Method of Determining Tire–Soil Interaction Parameters

Equations (41) to (43) and (53) to (101) express the parameters for wheel–soil interaction in terms of the parameters of the tire, soil and rolling conditions. Let us determine the order in which these equations are to be solved.

The initial data for determining these parameters shall be taken to be the depth of the rut formed by the wheel $h$, the slippage coefficient $\delta_s$, the tire parameters $R$, $B$, $H$, $b_t$, $p_w$, $k_t$, $m$, and $\Delta_t$ and the soil parameters $E$, $H_s$, $c_0$, $\phi_0$, $E_r'$, $E'$ and $\gamma$.

1. For condition $x=0$, we have $z=h$, $\alpha=0$, $\beta=\pm\phi_0$ for $\delta_s>0$; $\beta=\phi_0$ for $\delta_s<0$; $\beta=-\phi_0$ for $\delta_s=0$, $\beta=0$. From equations (14), (15), (73), (79), (65), (67), (85), (87), (86) and (93), we shall determine $X_1$, $X_2$, $I_{x1}$, $I_{x2}$, $k_{\beta1}$, $k_{\beta2}$, $q_s$, $q$, $\delta$, $x_1$, $x_2$, $\xi$ and $R_{w0}$ respectively.

2. The horizontal projection of the line of contact shall be divided into $n_x$ parts

$$\Delta=\frac{x_2-x_1}{n_x}; \quad x=\Delta xi,$$

where $i$ is the number of any part in successive order.

For each of the parts, we shall consecutively determine $z$ from equation (84); $\tan\alpha$ from equation (83); $\tan\beta$ from equation (82); $q_{sx}$ from equations (14), (15), (73), (79); $q_1$, $q_2$ and $q$ from equation (65); $\delta$ from equation (67); $\alpha_\delta$ from equation (68); $r_s$ from equation (69); $b_s$ from equation (70); $b_{con}$ from equation (71); $j$ from equations (90), (91); and $\tau_x$ from equation (88).

3. Using a numerical integration technique, we shall obtain $G_w$, $T$ and $M_w$ from equations (41) to (43).

4. The components of rolling resistance are determined as follows: $P_{fg}$ from equation (97), $P_{ft}$ from equation (100) and $P_{fa}$ from equation (101).

If $G_w$ and $T$ are the values given as the initial data instead of $h$ and $\delta_s$, then the procedure is to select several values of $h$ and $\delta_s$ from which $G_w$ and $T$ are determined. Graphs of $G_w=G_w(h)$ and $T=T(h)$ are then plotted for different values of $\delta_s$ (Fig. 41). Horizontal lines corresponding to the given values of $G_w$ and $T$ are drawn on the diagram. The value of $h$ is obtained from the point of intersection of these lines with the curves $G_w=G_w(h)$ and $T=T(h)$ for each of the values of $\delta_s$.

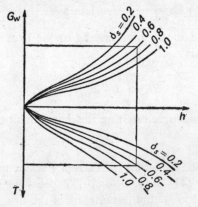

Fig. 41. Graphical determination of $h$ and $\delta_s$.

The above method may be used to determine all the parameters of tire-soil interaction and to analyze the influence of the principal tire and soil parameters on the tire–soil interaction parameters. When a detailed investigation of the shape of the contact surface and the distribution of soil reaction over the contact surface becomes necessary, one may make use of equations (53) to (66) and equation (81).

## A SIMPLIFIED METHOD OF DETERMINING TIRE–SOIL INTERACTION

The principal assumptions are:

The tire-soil contact surface consists of a flat zone, whose width is equal to the width of the tread and length is equal to the chord of the circle. The curvilinear zone consists of the toroid shaped surface of radius $R$ in the longitudinal section and $r_s$ in the lateral axial section (Fig. 42);

the average pressure over the curvilinear zone of contact is expressed in terms of the average pressure over the flat zone $q_p = \zeta_z q$;

soil deformation is determined from the average pressure over the flat zone of contact and the dimensions of the contact surface, which includes the curvilinear zone. This is suitably reduced to take the corresponding pressure and the direction in which the external load acts into account $\left( \tan \beta_0 = \dfrac{T}{G_w} \right)$.

The pressure over the flat zone of contact is obtained with the help of equation (67).

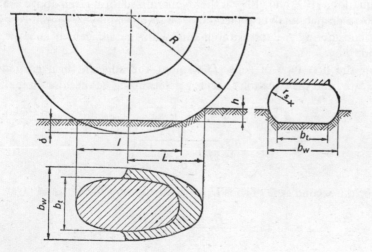

Fig. 42. Simplified representation of wheel–soil interaction.

The depth of the rut formed by the wheels is determined from equations (14) and (15), assuming $b = \sqrt{F}$ so that

$$q = \cfrac{1}{\cfrac{2}{\pi q_{s0}} \tan^{-1} \cfrac{\pi}{2} \cfrac{(H_s - h)}{b_t} + \cfrac{a}{EhI} \sqrt{F} \tan^{-1} \cfrac{H_s - h}{a\sqrt{F} \cos \beta}} . \qquad (102)$$

The area of the plane contact surface $F$ may be expressed in terms of the vertical load and the pressure as

$$F = \frac{G_w}{q} .$$

The bearing capacity of the soil $q_{s0}$ is determined from equation (18). Introducing coefficients $(K_{\beta 1}, K_{\beta 2})$ to take the direction in which the load acts into account and assuming $X_3 = 0$, we have

$$q_{s0} = K_{\beta 1} I_1 X_1 b_t + K_{\beta 2} I_2 X_2, \qquad (103)$$

where $K_{\beta 1}, K_{\beta 2}$ are obtained from equation (78);
$X_1, X_2$ from equation (14).

To determine $I_1$ and $I_2$, let us substitute $\dfrac{l}{b} = \dfrac{G_w}{q b_t^2}$ in equation (18), in which case

$$I_1 = \frac{G_w}{G_w + 0.4 q b_t^2}; \quad I_2 = \frac{G_w + q b_t^2}{G_w + 0.5 q b_t^2} . \qquad (104)$$

Equations (102) and (103) in their generalized form given above are solved for $h$ by a grapho-analytical method. The solution may be simplified by separately considering the soil without and with the adjacent firm layer of the ground.

For the first type of soils (I) without the adjacent firm ground layer, $H_s - h = \infty$, and the equation (102) for determining $h$ takes the simple form

$$h = \frac{\pi a \sqrt{\dfrac{G_w}{q}}}{2E \left( \dfrac{1}{q} - \dfrac{1}{q_{s0}} \right)} . \qquad (105)$$

For the second type of soils II, with an adjacent firm ground layer

$$\tan^{-1} \frac{H_s - h}{a\sqrt{F} \cos \beta} \approx \frac{H_s - h}{a\sqrt{F} \cos \beta};$$

$$\tan^{-1} \frac{\pi (H_s - h)}{2 b_t} \approx \frac{\pi (H_s - h)}{2 b_t} .$$

Substituting these expressions in equation (102) and rewriting it for $h$, we have

$$h = h_{\mathrm{E}} + \sqrt{h_{\mathrm{E}}^2 + \frac{q_{s0}\, b_t\, H_s}{E}}, \tag{106}$$

where

$$h_{\mathrm{E}} = \frac{1}{2}\left[ H_s - q_{s0}\, b_t \left( \frac{1}{E} + \frac{\cos\beta}{q} \right) \right].$$

For soils where the layer undergoing deformation is thin $\left( H_s < \frac{1}{2}\, b_t \right)$, one may assume that $\dfrac{1}{q_{s0}} = 0$ so that

$$h = \frac{q H_s}{q + E \cos\beta}. \tag{107}$$

The dimensions of the flat zone and the external contour of the contact surface are easily determined from the known values of $h$ and $\delta$ (see Fig. 42). For the flat zone $b = b_t$

$$l - 2\sqrt{(2R - \delta)\,\delta}, \tag{108}$$

and for the external contour

$$L = \sqrt{(2R - \delta - h)(h + \delta)}; \tag{109}$$

$$b_w = b_t + 2 b_s. \tag{110}$$

The value of $b_s$ is obtained from equations (68) to (70).

Assuming the contact surface to be elliptical in shape, the bearing capacity of the tire for the given value of $\delta$ may be obtained from the pressure and dimensions of the contact surface as,

$$G_w = \frac{\pi}{4}\, q \left[ l b_t + \zeta_z \left( L b_w - \frac{1}{2}\, l b_t \right) \right], \tag{111}$$

where

$$\zeta_z = \frac{q_s}{q};$$

$q_s$ is the average pressure over the curved zone of contact, approximately equal to the pressure corresponding to a sinkage depth of $\frac{2}{3} h$.

For type $I$ soils,

$$\zeta_z \approx \frac{E h + b_t\, q_s}{E h + 2 b_t\, q_s}. \tag{112}$$

For type *II* soils,

$$\zeta_z \approx \frac{H_s - h}{2H_s - h}.$$  (113)

The rolling resistance of the wheel may be obtained from the work done in forming the ruts

$$P_{fg} = \frac{A_s}{s} = \int_0^h qb_{con}\, dz.$$

For *I* type soils, where there is no adjacent firm ground layer, substituting the value of $q$ from equation (21), we have

$$P_{fg} = 2Eq_{s0}\, b_{con} \left( \frac{h}{2E} - \frac{\pi q_{s0}\, b_{con}}{4E^2} \ln \frac{2Eh + \pi q_{s0}\, b_{con}}{\pi q_{s0}\, b_{con}} \right),$$  (114)

where $b_{con} = b_t + 2\zeta_z b_s$.

For *II* type soils, which have a neighboring firm ground layer, from equation (106), we have

$$q = \frac{Ehq_{s0}\, b_{con} \cos \beta}{(H_s - h)(Eh + q_{s0}\, b_{con})}.$$

Substituting this value in the equation for $P_{fg}$, we have

$$P_{fg} = \frac{\pi q_{s0}\, Eb_{con}^2 \cos \beta}{2EH_s + \pi q_{s0}\, b_{con}} \left[ H_s \ln \frac{H_s}{H_s - h} - \frac{\pi q_{s0}\, b_{con}}{2E} \ln \frac{2Eh + \pi q_{s0}\, b_{con}}{\pi q_{s0}\, b_{con}} \right].$$  (115)

Components $P_{ft}$ and $P_{fa}$ of the resistance to rolling are obtained using equations (100) and (101).

Parameters $j$ and $q$ of the soil and tire may be assumed to be identical over the entire contact zone for an approximate evaluation of the adhesive force as a function of slippage. The nonuniform distribution of $j$ over the contact length can be accounted for by the coefficient $\zeta_j$. Then using equation (88), we have for the entire wheel

$$P_a = \tau F = \frac{G_w}{q} \left[ \frac{m}{\dfrac{1}{q\phi_r} + \dfrac{\zeta_j}{E_r' j}} + \frac{1 - m}{\dfrac{1}{q \tan \phi_0 + c_0 \zeta} + \dfrac{\zeta_j t}{E' j}} \right].$$

Substituting $j = \delta_s L_w$ and $L_w = \dfrac{G_w}{qb_t}$ in the above expression, we finally have

$$P_a = \frac{G_w}{q} \left[ \frac{m}{\dfrac{1}{q\phi_r} + \dfrac{\zeta_j qb_t}{E_r' \delta_s G_w}} + \frac{1 - m}{\dfrac{1}{q \tan \phi_0 + c_0 \zeta} + \dfrac{\zeta_j qb_t t}{E' \delta_s G_w}} \right],$$  (116)

where
$$\zeta=\left(1-\frac{G_\mathrm{w}\,\delta_\mathrm{s}}{q_\mathrm{t}\,b_\mathrm{t}}\right)\geqslant 0;$$

$$\zeta_\mathrm{j}=2-3.$$

Even simpler mathematical expression, accounting approximately for a few of the factors which greatly affect the wheel-soil interaction parameters, are useful for preliminary estimates.

Neglecting the effect of the dimensions of the contact surface on the bearing capacity of the soil and rolling conditions, using the most simple expression for the width of the plate contact zone

$$b=2\sqrt{B\delta}.$$

Introducing averaged coefficients for calculating the adhesive force and rolling resistance, the following expression is arrived at:

$$\left.\begin{aligned}
q &=\frac{p_\mathrm{w}+k_\mathrm{t}}{b_\mathrm{t}}\sqrt{B\delta}; \\[6pt]
h_\mathrm{I} &=\frac{ab_\mathrm{t}\,qq_\mathrm{s}}{E\,(q_\mathrm{s}-q)}; \\[6pt]
h_\mathrm{II} &=\frac{qH_\mathrm{s}}{E+q}; \\[6pt]
G_\mathrm{w} &=2.5\,(p_\mathrm{w}+k_\mathrm{t})\,\sqrt{DB}\,(\delta+0.5\,\zeta_\mathrm{z}\,h); \\[6pt]
P_\mathrm{a} &=\frac{G_\mathrm{w}}{q}\left(\frac{1}{\dfrac{1}{\tau_{\max}}+\dfrac{\zeta_\mathrm{j}\,qb_\mathrm{t}}{E'\,G_\mathrm{w}\,\delta_\mathrm{s}}}\right); \\[6pt]
P_\mathrm{fg} &=\zeta_\mathrm{z}\,qhb_\mathrm{t};\quad P_\mathrm{ft}=k_\mathrm{t}\,b_\mathrm{t}\,\delta; \\[6pt]
P_\mathrm{fa} &=\left(b_\mathrm{t}+2h\right)\frac{x_1^2\,p_\mathrm{a}}{2R_\mathrm{w0}},
\end{aligned}\right\} \tag{117}$$

where $h_\mathrm{I}$ and $h_\mathrm{II}$ are the respective depths of sinkage of a plate in a soil with and without an adjacent firm soil layer,

$$\tau_{\max}=q\left[m\phi_\mathrm{r}+\left(1-m\right)\left(\tan\phi_0+\frac{c_0}{q}\right)\right].$$

## THE PARAMETERS FOR EVALUATING THE WORKING CONDITIONS OF A WHEEL

A wheel which forms one of the components of a mobile machine performs the following functions. It acts as a supporting element transmitting the vertical load from the automobile to the road. It provides for the initiation of the external force (traction) necessary for the motion of the automobile. It acts as the principal component giving rise to external forces which transform the linear motion of the automobile to a curvilinear one. It acts as one of the power transmission and elastic components between the road and the suspension.

The loading capacity of a wheel may be evaluated by the sinkage parameter

$$P_s = \frac{\delta + h}{R} \tag{118}$$

and the coefficient of rolling resistance

$$f = \frac{P_{fg} + P_{ft} + P_{fa}}{G_w}. \tag{119}$$

The sinkage parameter, $P_s$, represents the possibility for a machine to move without the chassis brushing against the ground, while coefficient $f$ represents the effectiveness of utilization of the wheel.

The tractive capacity of a wheel is estimated by the traction coefficient

$$\phi_T = \frac{T}{G_w} = \frac{P_a - P_{fg}}{G_w}. \tag{120}$$

The traction coefficient is also used for evaluating the bearing traction road mobility. The ability of a wheel to surmount obstacles may be estimated from the threshold height of the uneven terrain described by the equation

$$h_{ob} = R \left( 1 - \frac{1}{\sqrt{1 + \phi_T^2}} \right). \tag{121}$$

The efficiency of the driving wheel is often evaluated by the expression

$$\eta = \frac{\phi_T (1 - \delta_s)}{\phi_T + f}. \tag{122}$$

However, the work done by the wheel is not wholly confined to the driving mode for which the tractive force must always be positive. In actual motion conditions in a multi-wheeled automobile, a part of the wheel often operates under free-wheeling, neutral drive or even braking modes when $\phi_T \leqslant 0$. If the wheel operates under such conditions, the expression for efficiency given by equation (122) becomes unsuitable.

A more comprehensive equation for wheel efficiency may be obtained from an expression which comprises the ratio of power expended on rolling to the load and the speed,

$$P_e = \frac{N}{v G_w}.$$

In general, the power expended on the rolling of the wheel consists of the deformation of soil $N_g$, the radial deformation of tires $N_t$, slippage $N_s$, the tangential deformation of tires $N_\tau$, the overcoming adhesion of soil $N_a$ and the overcoming of the gradient of the path $N_\alpha$:

$$N = N_g + N_t + N_s + N_\tau + N_a + N_\alpha.$$

Experimental investigations, conducted by V.A. Petrushov [46], show that the power expended on the radial deformation of a tire is

$$N_t = \frac{G_w \, v f_t \, R_{w0}}{R_{w0} - \lambda M_w},$$

where $\lambda$ is a coefficient for the tangential elasticity of the wheel provided with an elastic tire.

The quantity $(N_s + N_\tau)$ may be obtained from the expression

$$N_s + N_\tau = M_w \left( \frac{v}{R_w} - \frac{v}{R_{w0}} \right).$$

Let us express the rolling radius $R_w$ in terms of the slippage coefficient $\delta_s$, where the slip is considered together with the tangential deformation of the tire and soil,

$$R_w = R_{w0} \, (1 - \delta_s).$$

The turning moment applied at the wheel may be expressed by the equation,

$$M_w = G_w \, (\psi + \phi_T) \, (R_{w0} - \lambda M_w),$$

where $\psi$ is a coefficient for the road resistance given by $\psi = f + \sin \alpha'$.

Substituting the values of $R_w$ and $M_w$ in the expression for $(N_s + N_\tau)$, we have

$$(N_s + N_\tau) = \frac{G_w v \, (\psi + \phi_T) \, (R_{w0} - \lambda M_w) \, \delta_s}{R_{w0} \, (1 - \delta_s)}.$$

The rest of the components which account for loss in power are given by the following equations:

$$N_g = G_w \, f_g \, v; \quad N_a = G_w \, f_a \, v; \quad N_\alpha = G_w \, v \sin \alpha',$$

where $f_g$ and $f_a$ are the coefficients for the resistance to rolling brought about by the deformation of the soil and the adhesion of the soil to the tire;

$\alpha'$ is the angle representing the gradient of the path.

Substituting the values of $N_t$, $(N_s + N_\tau)$, $N_g$, $N_a$ and $N_\alpha$ in the efficiency expression $P_e$, we have

$$P_e = \sin \alpha' + f_g + f_a + f_t \frac{R_{w0}}{R_{w0} - \lambda M_w} + \frac{(\psi + \phi_T)\, \delta_s\, (R_{w0} - \lambda M_w)}{R_{w0}\, (1 - \delta_s)}. \quad (123)$$

The equation for determining all quantities except the coefficient $\lambda$ appearing in equation (123) has been given above.

The coefficient $\lambda$ is usually determined experimentally from the graph $R_w = R_w (M_w)$, using the initial linear portion of this graph (Fig. 43). The value of $\lambda$ obtained in this manner on hard dry soil lies approximately between 0.005 and 0.015 mm/(kg·m).

Depending upon the turning moment, the rolling radius reduces not only because of the tangential deformation of the tire but, to a much larger extent, due to the slippage of the tire relative to the road and the tangential deformation of the soil. Hence the value of $\lambda$, obtained experimentally as described above, does not exactly represent the characteristic tangential elasticity of the tire. It depends not only on the structure of the tire but also on the state of the road (soil).

The nature of the variation of the rolling radius only as a function of the tangential deformation of the tire is shown by curve 2 in Fig. 43. The non-linear nature of this curve is explained by the deformation properties of rubber under compression (with an increase of deformation, the modulus of elasticity of rubber increases). Hence, the actual value of $\lambda$ is less than that shown above and significantly decreases with an increase of $M_w$.

In this connection, one may assume $\lambda \approx 0$, which considerably simplifies the expression for $P_e$. Taking $\sin \alpha' + f_g + f_t + f_a = \psi$, we have

$$P_e \cong \frac{\psi + \phi_T\, \delta_s}{1 - \delta_s}. \quad (124)$$

The error caused by such a simplification does not exceed 5%. Equation (124) is applicable for all modes of the wheel's rolling.

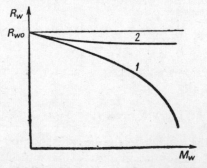

Fig. 43. Variation of the rolling radius as a function of the moment $M_w$:
1—taking slip into consideration; 2—without taking slip into consideration.

In case of total skidding, $\delta_s = 1$, $P_e = \infty$ and in case of pure rolling, $\delta_s = 0$ and $P_e = \psi$. When the wheel motion is accompanied by slip $\delta_s = -1$:

$$\phi_T = -(\phi + \sin \alpha'); \quad \psi = \phi + \sin \alpha'; \quad P_e = \phi + \sin \alpha'.$$

The functional relationship $P_e = P_e\ (\phi_T)$, shown in Fig. 44, gives the tractive-efficiency characteristics of a wheel over a given soil.

An averaged value of $P_{e\ av}$, defined by the expression

$$P_{e\ av} = \frac{1}{s} \sum_{i=1}^{i=n} P_{ei} S_i, \tag{125}$$

may be used for evaluating the possible tractive-efficiency of a wheel on a route consisting of various types of road conditions and soil tracts. Here $S_i$ is the length of the $i$th part of the path and $s$ is the total length of the route.

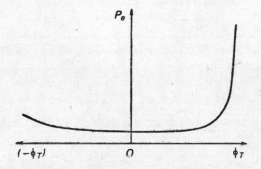

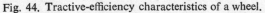

Fig. 44. Tractive-efficiency characteristics of a wheel.

The effectiveness of a wheel as a controlling element is evaluated in terms of the lateral force as a function of the drift angle $P_s = P_s\ (\delta_d)$ as shown in Fig. 45. The principal factors in this relationship are the coefficient of resistance of the lateral drift $K'$, representing the linear portion of the expression

$$K' = \frac{P_s}{\delta_d}$$

and the adhesion coefficient for the wheel-soil in the lateral direction

$$\phi_s = \frac{P_{s\ max}}{G_w}.$$

The effectiveness of the wheel as an elastic element may be evaluated by the magnitude of the effective rigidity of the tire-soil system,

$$c'_{eff} = \frac{c'_g c'_t}{c'_g + c'_t},$$

where $c'_g$ is the firmness of the soil;
$\quad c'_t$ is the rigidity of the tire.

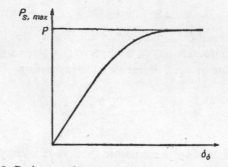

Fig. 45. Resistance characteristics of a tire for lateral drift.

Frequently, it becomes necessary to evaluate the properties of a wheel or tire unrelated to the actual condition of the soil surface. In such cases, one may use certain specific parameters to evaluate the performance of the wheel from the point of view of mobility, versatility, design effectiveness, lateral stability and elastic properties.

The parameters of each of these factors are given below:

*Mobility.* Minimum pressure on soil $q_{min} = p_{w\ min} + k_t$; ratio of vertical load to the midsection $\dfrac{G_w}{BD}$; saturation coefficient of the tread pattern, $m$ and the radius of wheel $R$.

*Versatility.* Variation range of the internal pressure of the tires ($p_{w\ max} - p_{w\ min}$) and the saturation coefficient of the tread pattern $m$.

*Design effectiveness.* The volume of the wheel referred to a unit area of the contact surface $\dfrac{V_w}{F_{max}}$, the coefficient of resistance to the rolling over a hard road surface at pressure $p_{w\ max}$ and $p_{w\ min}$.

*Lateral stability.* The coefficient of resistance to lateral drift $K'$ on a dry, hard road surface.

*Elastic properties.* The rigidity of the tire under normal internal air pressure for hard road surface conditions

$$c'_t = \frac{G_w}{\delta} \approx \frac{G_w}{0.13H}.$$

# CHAPTER 3

# The Effect of Wheel Parameters on Performance

The effective utilization of a wheel as a tractive device depends on its parameters, which may vary during the course of operation (internal air pressure, vertical load on the wheel, speed) as well as on the design parameters, which are invariant during operation (dimensions of the wheel, design of the tread, construction of the carcass, etc.).

Performance parameters can be easily ascertained from experimental investigations, since during such tests one of the parameters may vary, keeping all others constant. Up to now, a large amount of experimental data has been collected on the influence of air pressure in tires and the vertical load on the performance characteristics of the wheel. The effect of speed on wheel performance has been investigated to a lesser extent.

Experimental investigation of the effect of wheel design parameters on performance demands considerable expenditure and is beset with many technical difficulties due to the complexities involved in developing several sets of tires each differing from the other by only a single parameter, which has to be investigated. The experimental data needed to ascertain the influence of design parameters on wheel performance are small and, hence, in most cases the data are obtained without imposing the condition that all other parameters should be constant.

The analysis of performance parameters is mainly based on experimental data; while the results of theoretical investigations are utilized for generalizing and explaining problems which are outside the scope of experimental investigations. On the other hand, the analysis of design parameters is mainly based on the results of theoretical investigations and the experimental data are used only to confirm the basic theoretical assumptions.

## EFFECT OF TIRE DIMENSIONS

Let us consider three variants of tire size for increasing the effective utilization of the wheel under difficult road conditions.

*Variant I.* The dimensions of the tire profile remain constant. Only the outer and landing diameters of the tire are increased (Fig. 46).

*Variant II.* The landing diameter of the tire remains constant, while the width and height of the tire profile are increased so that their ratio remains constant.

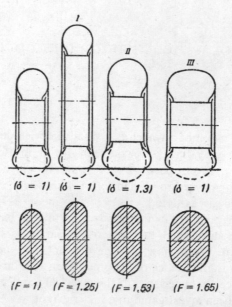

Fig. 46. Three variants for increasing tire dimensions (*F*—contact area for maximum allowable radial deformation): *I, II, III*—variants.

*Variant III.* The outer and landing diameters of the tire are maintained constant, while the width of the tire profile is increased.

A comparison of these variants (Fig. 46) shows that for identical volumes of tires, the maximum contact area is provided by the variant *III* and the maximum range of variation of radial deformation and pressure is provided by the variant *II.*

For a more comprehensive analysis, we shall use the results obtained from a consideration of the physical interaction between the wheel and the soil given by equations (41) to (101) and (118) to (121). The 12.00–18 tire shall be taken as the standard for comparison purposes. In all cases, the vertical load on the wheel is taken to be 1500 kg.

## Effect of Outer Diameter

When the outside diameter of the tire is expanded (variant *I*), the length and corresponding contact surface over a hard surface increase, and the pressure exerted on the road decreases to some extent. As a result, the adhesion between the tire and the soil increases and the slip diminishes.

The rolling resistance of a wheel on a smooth hard surface reduces slightly with an increase in the outer tire diameter, since the curvature of the spherical tire surface somewhat decreases. The resistance to motion on uneven surfaces reduces significantly when the outer tire diameter is increased. According to the diagram shown in Fig. 47, for $M_w = 0$

$$f_{ob} = \frac{T_{ob}}{G_w} = \frac{\sqrt{(2R - h_{ob} - \delta)(h_{ob} + \delta)}}{R - h_{ob} - \delta}, \tag{126}$$

where $T_{ob}$ is the tractive force necessary to overcome obstacles in the path;
$h_{ob}$ is the height of the obstacle.

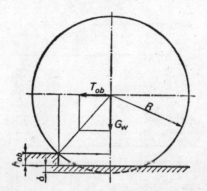

Fig. 47. Force required to overcome an obstacle.

On soft soils, an increase of the outer tire diameter in most cases does not lead to an increase in the contact length as the wheel is less apt to sink into the soil. It may, on the other hand, to some extent lead to a reduction of contact length. This is explained by the far more uniform pressure exerted by a tire with a larger outer diameter.

The adhesion between wheel and soil varies as a function of the outer tire diameter and is different for different soils depending upon their properties. If the adhesive properties of the soil increase with sinkage, then for an increase in the outer diameter, the adhesion decreases and the tractive force at the hitch point is also likewise reduced. If the adhesive properties do not change along the depth then, as a rule, when the outer diameter is increased, the adhesive force between tire and soil slightly increases. This is due to the more uniform pressure distribution and a lessening tendency for the tangential forces at the contact surface to go in different directions.

If there is an increase in the outer diameter the rolling resistance of the wheel reduces on all soils. The coefficient $f_g = \dfrac{P_{fg}}{G_w}$ reduces due to both the reduction in the depth of the rut that is formed as well as to the reduction in the bulldozer action. The softer the soil and more uneven the path, the more effective is the increase in the outer diameter. The height of the obstacles that can be surmounted increases in proportion to the radius of the wheel.

82

The qualitative effect of the outer diameter on the performance of the wheel on a plowed field, obtained from equations (41) to (101) and (118) to (121), is illustrated in Fig. 48.

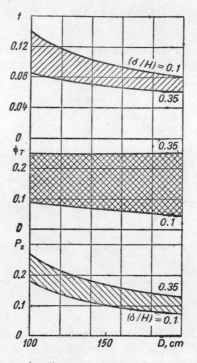

Fig. 48. Effect of an outer tire diameter on the performance parameters of a wheel ($B=29$ cm; $G_w=1500$ kg; soil type—plowed loamy soil).

When the outer tire diameter $D$ is increased, and there is a small deformation of the tire ($v_1 = \dfrac{\delta}{H} = 0.1$), there is a noticeable change in the traction and off-the-road mobility index $\phi_T$. It becomes even much smaller for a large tire deformation ($v_1 = 0.35$).

The effect of the outer tire diameter on the efficiency of the wheel, governed by the value of $f$ for $\phi_T = 0$, is highly significant. When the diameter is increased from 100 to 200 cm, efficiency increases by 35 to 60%. An increase of the outer tire diameter has the most significant effect on the sinkage parameter $P_s$.

The disadvantages of increasing the outer diameter include the considerable increase in the mass and moment of the inertia of the wheel as also the increase in the height of the center of gravity of the machine. The mass of the tire $m_t$ and its moment of inertia $J_t$ may be expressed by the equations:

$$m_t = \pi g_{\text{prof}} (D - \varepsilon H); \tag{127}$$

$$J_t = m_t \, (R - \varepsilon_1 H)^2, \tag{128}$$

where $g_{prof}$ is the mass of the tire referred to a unit length of its outer circumference (profile);

$\varepsilon$ and $\varepsilon_1$ are constants.

### Effect of Tire Profile Width for $H = B$

An increase of the tire profile width for $H = B$ (variant *II*) and a constant diameter of the rim leads to an increase in the maximum permissible radial deformation and outer diameter of the tire. In this case, the contact surface increases both in length and breadth (see Fig. 46). The rolling resistance of the wheel on a hard road increases slightly due to an increase in slippage at the contact surface as well as an increase in the mass of rubber and cord subjected to deformation. Adhesive force, as a rule, increases on dry roads and may either increase or decrease on wet surfaces.

On deformable soils, an increase in the width and height of the profile significantly reduces the pressure and, correspondingly, the depth of the ruts. The rolling resistance of the wheel is governed inversely by the depth and width of the ruts formed by the wheels. In most cases, the depth of the rut plays the dominant role and, hence, its decrease leads to a fall in the rolling resistance. However, on soils which have a very weak top layer on a hard subsurface, rolling resistance may even increase since an increase in the depth of the rut is very small; while its width is considerable. As a result, resistance to rolling due to the tire's deformation thereby increases. Hence, the total rolling resistance as a function of profile width may have a minimum.

With an increase in the value of $B$, the wheel-soil adhesion usually increases in conformity with the increase of the contact area and the internal adhesion $c_0$ of the soil. But the soil surfaces with sharply changing frictional properties are the exception to this (for example, on an argillaceous soil surface immediately after rain a lower tire inflation sometimes leads to a reduction in adhesion).

Figure 49 shows the relationship between the performance parameters of the wheel and the profile width $B$ of the tire. It may be observed from this figure that on a wet loamy soil with a 30 cm thick deformable top layer, the performance characteristics of the wheel significantly improve when profile width $B$ is increased from 20 to 30 cm. When $B$ is further increased, only the traction coefficient $\phi_T$ increases; while the rest of the parameters hardly change. On other types of soils, the nature of these relationships differs considerably from each other.

### Effect of the Profile Width for $H = $ const. and $D = $ const.

Increasing the size of the tire by increasing only the profile width (variant *III*) leads to an increase in the contact width without affecting its length. In

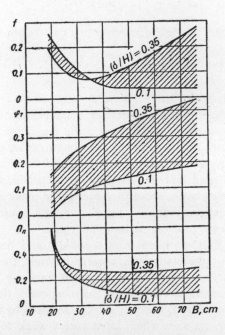

Fig. 49. Effect of tire profile width $B\,(H=B)$ on the performance parameters of the wheel ($d=46$ cm, $G_w=1500$ kg; soil type—plowed loamy field).

such a case, the increase in the contact area is almost proportional to the increase in the width of the profile. The maximum permissible deformation of the tire remains unaltered. Since there is no change in the outer diameter and the contact length, there is no improvement in the ability to overcome vertical obstacles in the path.

The nature of variation of the rolling resistance and the wheel-soil adhesion with the profile width is similar to that of the previous case (variant $II$).

The magnitudes of the performance parameters of the wheel as a function of the profile width are shown in Fig. 50.

For the three types of soils under consideration, the characteristic feature is the improvement in the performance parameters with the increase of the profile width. The traction coefficient $\phi_T$ increases sharply on the weakest of the soils (snow and waterlogged meadows) and slightly less so on moist loamy soils. The effect of the profile width on efficiency is well-defined for smaller tire deformation $\left(\dfrac{\delta}{H}=0.1\right)$. With an increase of deformation, this effect is reduced and may even become negative on compact surfaces (Fig. 50).

The effect of the profile width on the sinkage parameter $P_s$ increases with the increase of soil deformation.

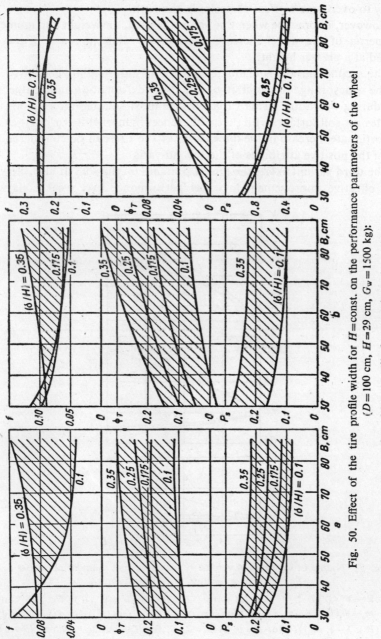

Fig. 50. Effect of the tire profile width for $H$=const. on the performance parameters of the wheel ($D$=100 cm, $H$=29 cm, $G_w$=1500 kg):

a—plowed loamy soil; b—waterlogged meadow; c—snow.

Let us compare the three above variants for increasing tire dimensions.

The first variant provides the maximum road clearance and a greater ability to overcome vertical obstacles in the path.

However, in practice when this variant is used, the weight and moment of the inertia of the wheel increase considerably and the center of gravity is located at a greater height.

The second variant is characterized by its universal applicability i.e., it has the widest range of variation of radial tire deformation and contact pressure during operation. This variant is the most suitable for running automobiles on soil surfaces with sharp differences in mechanical properties. The proportionate increase in the dimensions of the tire can be considered to be one of the positive attributes of the second variant.

The third variant exerts the lowest pressure on the soil. It also shows the most effective improvement in wheel performance over weak soils where

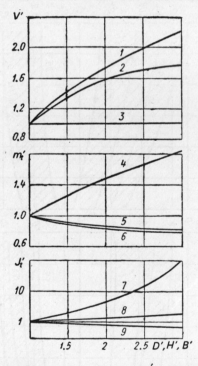

Fig. 51. Nature of variation of volume $V'$, mass $m_t'$ and moment of inertia $J_t'$ of a tire as a function of its dimensions:

$1$—$V'=V'(D')$; $2$—$V'=V'(H')$ for $H=B$; $3$—$V'=V'(B')$ for $H=$const.; $4$—$m_t'=m_t'(D')$; $5$—$m_t'=m_t'(B')$ for $H=$const.; $6$—$m_t'=m_t'(H')$ for $H=B$; $7$—$J_t'=J_t'(D')$; $8$—$J_t'=J_t'(H')$ for $H=B$; $9$—$J_t'=J_t'(B')$for $H=$const. ($D'$, $B'$ and $H'$ are the fractional increments of the corresponding diameter, width and height of the tire profile).

friction properties do not increase with depth. However, it suffers from lack of universal applicability. A large increase of the profile width results in a more difficult configuration of the machine.

Figure 51 shows the specific indices for volume $\left( V' = \dfrac{V_t}{V_{t0}} \right)$, mass $\left( m_t' = \dfrac{m_t}{m_{t0}} \right)$ and moment of inertia $\left( J_t' = \dfrac{J_t}{J_{t0}} \right)$ for the three above considered variants.

These indices affect the mass and overall dimensions of the machine, its smooth running as well as the transmission load.

When only the profile width is increased (variant *III*), the specific volume index does not change; whereas the specific mass and specific moment of inertia of the tire slightly decrease. With an increase of the outer tire diameter (variant *I*), the indices of specific volume, mass and moment of inertia increase considerably. The second variant occupies a position in between these two so far as these indices are concerned. When the width of the circular profile is increased ($H = B$), the specific volume index increases (which, however, is less than that of the first variant), the specific mass index decreases almost to the same extent as in the third variant; while the specific moment of the inertia index slightly increases.

As can be observed from above, the third variant is preferable as far as the specific volume and mass indices are concerned. In this case, the profile width changes without any change in its height. However, the shape of the profile undergoes a change.

## EFFECT OF THE TIRE PROFILE SHAPE

With the present level of development of the tire manufacturing industry, it is possible to have a wide and varied range of tire profile shapes.

Firstly, the profile shape significantly changes with a change in the rim width: perimeter ratio. Figure 52b shows balanced configurations of tire profiles for $\dfrac{B_F}{U} = 0.64$ and $\dfrac{B_F}{U} = 0.2$ where the tire cord placement is meridional ($\beta = 0$).

Secondly, the shape of the tire profile varies, depending upon the angle $\beta_w$ subtended by the tire cord (Fig. 52a).

Thirdly, there is a very high probability for alteration in the tire profile when its equilibrium is violated due to the use of a girdle ring (Fig. 52c).

In general, the shape of the tire profile may be characterized by the parameter $\dfrac{H}{B}$. In the well-known types of tires, this parameter varies between 1.1 and 0.2. It should be remembered that the relative height of the tire profile may be decreased to any extent by increasing the rim width and using a girdle

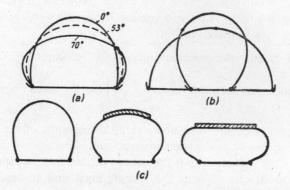

Fig. 52. Methods of altering tire profile shape: a—changing the angle of inclination of the tire cord; b—changing the width of the rim ($\beta_w=0$); c—using a girdle
ring.

ring. The maximum value of $\dfrac{H}{B}$ is limited only by the configuration of the
profile.

A comprehensive analysis of the shape of the tire profile can be carried out
using the system of equations (53) to (60). With the help of these equations,
it is possible to analyze the effect of variation of not only the parameter $\dfrac{H}{B}$
but also the sidewall parameters ($H_s$, $l_s$) and tread parameters ($h_t$, $b_t$) on the
radial flexibility and contact surface parameters.

Let us consider the effect of the profile shape $\left(\text{parameter } \dfrac{H}{B}\right)$ on the dimensions of the contact surface and the radial deformation of a tire for the
following conditions:

the sum of the width and height of the profile remains constant ($B+H=$
const.);

the angle of deflection of the sidewall per unit length during deformation
of the profile remains constant to ensure identical operating conditions for the
sidewalls $\left(\dfrac{\alpha_s-\alpha_{s0}}{l_s}=4\right)$;

the ratios $\dfrac{h_t}{H}=0.15$, $\dfrac{b_t}{B}=0.8$, $\dfrac{D}{H+B}=2$ and $\rho=0$ are assumed to be constant.

Figure 53 shows the shape of the profile in an undeformed condition for
the $\dfrac{H}{B}$ ratios equal to 1, 0.75, 0.5 and 0.25.

Figure 54 shows the variation of several performance parameters as a

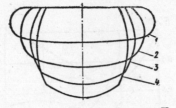

Fig. 53. Shape of tire profile for various $\dfrac{H}{B}$ ratios:

$1-\dfrac{H}{B}=0.25;\ 2-\dfrac{H}{B}=0.5;\ 3-\dfrac{H}{B}=0.75;\ 4-\dfrac{H}{B}=1\ \left(B+H=\text{const.};\ \dfrac{h_t}{H}=0.15\ \text{and}\ \dfrac{B_F}{B}=0.8\right).$

function of the profile shape. It may be observed from Fig. 54 that when $\dfrac{H}{B}$ is decreased $\dfrac{qb}{\delta}$ and $\dfrac{qF}{\delta}$, the rigidity of the profile and tire progressively increase. The contact width increases, but its length decreases. The fractional contact surface $\left(F'=\dfrac{F}{H+B}\right)$ becomes a maximum for $\dfrac{H}{B}\approx 0.5$. When $\dfrac{H}{B}$ is reduced from 1 to 0.5, the contact area increases by 30% while the fractional flexibility of the sidewalls $\left(\delta'_s=\dfrac{\delta_s}{H+B}\right)$ and the tread $\left(\delta'_t=\dfrac{\delta_t}{H+B}\right)$ reduces by 65%.

Thus, when the perimeter of the profile and the outer diameter are kept invariant, the contact area can be increased by reducing $\dfrac{H}{B}$ up to 0.5. However, in such a case, it is impossible to avoid a reduction in the radial flexibility of the tire. When $\dfrac{H}{B}$ is reduced below 0.5, the contact area increases but the flexibility rapidly decreases.

The versatility of a tire can be gaged by the range of possible changes in pressures and profile widths during its operation. These parameters are governed by the permissible radial deformation of the tire. The greater the deformation, the greater the possibility of regulating the tire pressure. Consequently, it is advantageous to increase the $\dfrac{H}{B}$ ratio in order to improve the versatility of the tire.

The specific volume $v'_t$ of the tire (in the case where $D=\text{const.}$, $H+B=\text{const.}$) is a maximum for $\dfrac{H}{B}\approx 0.75$ (Fig. 55). When $\dfrac{H}{B}$ is reduced up to 0.25 the volume of the tire decreases by 25%; while the volume occupied by the wheel progressively increases. However, in this case, the diameter also increases and, correspondingly, the volume encompassed by the rim, which can then be utilized advantageously.

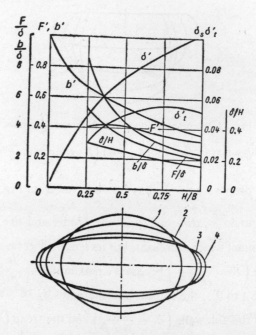

Fig. 54. Effect of profile shape $\left(\dfrac{H}{B}\right)$ on the deformability of a tire and contact surface parameters:

$$1-\frac{H}{B}=0.25; \quad 2-\frac{H}{B}=0.5; \quad 3-\frac{H}{B}=0.75; \quad 4-\frac{H}{B}=1.0 \ \left(B+H=\text{const.}, \ \frac{D}{H+B}=2, \right.$$

$$\left. \frac{h_t}{H}=0.15, \ \frac{b_t}{B}=0.8\right).$$

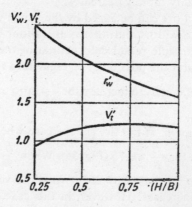

Fig. 55. Influence of $\dfrac{H}{B}$ on the volume of tire and wheel.

The energy expended on the deflection of the tire's sidewalls, which is governed by the internal friction of the tire, can be obtained by using the expression for potential energy of deflection as,

$$A_p = \frac{EJ\phi^2}{2l_s},$$

where $E$ is the modulus elasticity;

$J$ is the moment of inertia;

$\phi$ is the angle of rotation of the one end section relative to the other;

$l_s$ is the length of the arc.

For the sidewall

$$\phi_s = \alpha_s - \alpha_{s0};$$

$$A_{ps} = \frac{EJ(\alpha_s - \alpha_{s0})^2}{2l_s}.$$

For the tread portion

$$\phi_t = \frac{l_t}{r_t} = 2\sin^{-1}\frac{b_t}{2r_t};$$

$$A_{pt} = \frac{EJl_t}{2r_t^2}.$$

The total potential energy of deflection is

$$A_p = A_{ps} + A_{pt}.$$

The graph for the variation of $A_p' = A_p'\left(\frac{H}{B}\right)$ for the case under consideration is shown in Fig. 56 $\left(A_p' = \frac{2A_p}{EJ}\right)$. It is seen from Fig. 56 that when $\frac{H}{B}$ is decreased, the absolute energy loss $A_p$ and the energy loss per unit area $\frac{A_p}{F}$ significantly decrease; while the energy loss related to the unit radial deformation $\frac{A_p}{\delta}$ changes but little.

The sidewall curvature, which is characterized by its height to length ratio $\frac{H_s}{l_s}$, has a pronounced influence on the rigidity of a tire element as well as the entire tire. When the length of the sidewalls is increased, keeping their height and width of the tread constant, the rigidity of the tire element decreases. In such a case, the rigidity index for the entire tire takes a large curvature (Fig. 57).

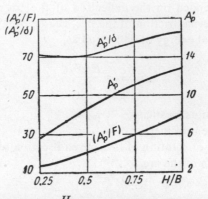

Fig. 56. Effect of $\dfrac{H}{B}$ on the internal losses of a tire.

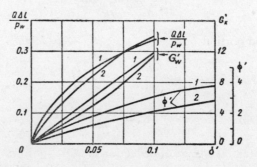

Fig. 57. Effect of the shape of a sidewall on the rigidity index:
$1-l_s'=0.45$; $2-l_s'=0.5$ ($H_s'=0.425$, $D'=2$, $b_t'=0.4$).

The effect of sidewall shape on its own durability can be estimated from the relationship between the angle of deflection $\phi'$ of the sidewall and the radial deformation which is shown in Fig. 57. When the initial curvature of the sidewalls is increased, the corresponding deflection per unit of radial deformation decreases. Consequently, the permissible radial deformation due to sidewall deflection must be increased.

The influence of rim width on the radial rigidity of the profile may be analyzed with the help of equations (53) to (60). Calculations show that for an increase of the difference ($B_F - b_t$), the rigidity of the element and its load bearing capacity increase slightly.

Consider the diagram shown in Fig. 58 to study the effect of the profile parameters on sidewall flexibility. The elementary radial force $dG_w$ and the elementary lateral force $dP_s$ act on the tire element. Under this action, the tire element deforms in the radial direction by $\delta$ and in the lateral direction by $\lambda_s$.

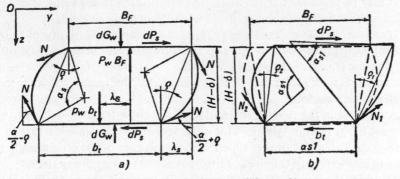

Fig. 58. Lateral deformation of the profile:

a—$B_F = b_t$; b—$B_F > b_t$.

Let us write one equation for the components of these forces along the $z$ and $y$ directions, acting on the tread, and another for their components in the $y$ direction, acting on the sidewall:

$$dl p_w b_t - dG_w = 2N \cos \frac{\alpha_s}{2} \cos \rho;$$

$$dP_s = 2N \cos \frac{\alpha_s}{2} \sin \rho;$$

$$dl p_w (H - \delta) = 2N \sin \frac{\alpha_s}{2} \cos \rho.$$

Let us express parameters $\rho$ and $\alpha$ in terms of parameters of the deformed profile (from geometrical relationships)

$$\tan \rho = \frac{\lambda_s}{H - \delta};$$

$$\alpha_s = 2 \sqrt{6 \left( 1 - \frac{\lambda_s^2 + (H - \delta)^2}{l_s} \right)}.$$

Solving these equations simultaneously, we have

$$\frac{dP_s}{\lambda_s} = \frac{dl p_w b_t - dG_w}{H - \delta}; \tag{129}$$

$$dG_w = p_w \left[ b_t - (H - \delta) \cot \sqrt{6 \left( 1 - \frac{\sqrt{(H - \delta)^2 + \lambda_s^2}}{l_s} \right)} \right] dl; \tag{130}$$

$$\frac{dP_s}{\lambda_s} = \left[ p_w \cot \sqrt{6 \left( 1 - \frac{\sqrt{(H - \delta)^2 + \lambda_s^2}}{l_s} \right)} \right] dl. \tag{131}$$

It may be observed that in equations (129) and (130), the value of $dG_w$ also includes the radial force acting on the element of the girdle ring.

It can be seen from equation (131) that the lateral flexibility of the tire element is governed both by the tire inflation pressure and the ratio of the chord to arc length of the sidewalls. The lateral rigidity of the profile reduces with an increase of radial deformation and slightly increases with an increase in lateral deformation.

A decrease in the ratio of sidewall height $H$ to its length $l_s$ must lead to a decrease in the lateral rigidity. This occurs when there is an increase in the girdling coefficient for tires of type $P$ and an increase of the crown angle (the angle of inclination of the tire cord to the carcass) for ordinary tires.

Consider the lateral deformation of a tire element shown in Fig. 58b to elucidate the effect of the difference $(B_F - b_t)$ on the lateral rigidity. It follows from this diagram that

$$dP_s = N_1 \sin\left(\frac{\alpha_{s1}}{2} + \rho_1\right) - N_2 \sin\left(\frac{\alpha_{s2}}{2} - \rho_2\right), \qquad (132)$$

where

$$N_1 = \frac{l_s}{\alpha_{s1}} p_w;$$

$$N_2 = \frac{l_s}{\alpha_{s2}} p_w;$$

$$\alpha_{s1} = 2\sqrt{6\left(1 - \frac{H - \delta}{l_s \cos\rho_1}\right)};$$

$$\alpha_{s2} = 2\sqrt{6\left(1 - \frac{H - \delta}{l_s \cos\rho_2}\right)};$$

$$\rho_1 = \tan^{-1}\frac{B_F - b_t + 2\lambda_s}{2(H - \delta)};$$

$$\rho_2 = \tan^{-1}\frac{B_F - b_t - 2\lambda_s}{2(H - \delta)}.$$

Figure 59 shows the graph of the function $\dfrac{dP_s}{p_w} = \dfrac{dP_s}{p_w}\left(\dfrac{B_F - b_t}{b_t}\right)$ obtained on the basis of these equations. The parameters selected for calculations were: $\dfrac{H_s}{b_t} = 0.5$, $\dfrac{l_s}{b_t} = 0.515$, $\dfrac{B_F - b_t}{b_t} = 0$ to $0.1$ and $\dfrac{\lambda_s}{b_t}$ equal to 0.05, 0.1 and 0.15. It may be observed from Fig. 59 that when $(B_F - b_t)$ is increased, the lateral rigidity progressively increases.

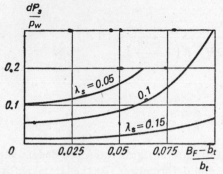

Fig. 59. Effect of the ratio of rim width to tread width on the lateral rigidity of the element.

Equation (131) should be integrated over the angle of contact between the tire and soil to obtain an expression for the lateral rigidity of the entire tire. Writing the radial deformation in terms of the angle $\alpha$ (see Fig. 40 for a hard road surface)

$$\delta = R\,(\cos\alpha - \cos\alpha_1)$$

and substituting the expression under the integral sign by an approximate function (which is integrated), we have

$$\cot\sqrt{6\left(1 - \frac{\sqrt{[H - R\,(\cos\alpha - \cos\alpha_1)]^2 + \lambda_s^2}}{l_s}\right)}$$

$$\approx \frac{0.375\,l_s}{1.1\,l_s - H - R\cos\alpha_1 + R\cos\alpha} - 0.8.$$

After integrating and rearranging the above expression, we have

$$\frac{P_s}{p_w\,\lambda_s} = 2\,Ra_s\left[\frac{0.375\,l_s}{\sqrt{R^2 - A^2}}\ln\frac{R - A\cos\alpha_1 + \sqrt{R^2 - A^2}\sin\alpha_1}{1.1\,l_s - H} - 0.8\,\alpha_1\right]\quad(133)$$

where $A = H + R\cos\alpha_1 - 1.1\,l_s + \dfrac{\lambda_s^2}{2H - R\cos\alpha_1}$;

$a_s$ is a coefficient for transformation to a real tire.

Substituting $\cos\alpha_1 = 1 - \dfrac{\delta}{R}$; $\alpha_1 = \sqrt{\dfrac{2\delta}{R}}$ and $\sin\alpha_1 = \sqrt{\left(2 - \dfrac{\delta}{R}\right)\dfrac{\delta}{R}}$ in equation (133), we have

$$\frac{P_s}{p_w\,\lambda_s} = 2Ra_s\left[\frac{0.375\,l_s}{\sqrt{R^2 - A^2}}\ln\frac{R - A\left(1 - \dfrac{\delta}{R}\right) + \sqrt{(R^2 - A^2)\left(2 - \dfrac{\delta}{R}\right)\dfrac{\delta}{R}}}{1.1\,l_s - H}\right.$$

$$\left. - 0.8\sqrt{\frac{2\delta}{R}}\right],\qquad(134)$$

where

$$A = H + R\left(1 - \frac{\delta}{R}\right) + \frac{\lambda_s^2}{2H - R\left(1 - \frac{\delta}{R}\right)} - 1.1\, l_s.$$

For small values of $\lambda_s$

$$A \approx H + R\left(1 - \frac{\delta}{R}\right) - 1.1\, l_s.$$

It follows from equation (134) that the lateral rigidity of a tire depends to a significant extent on its radius and radial deformation. As the lateral deformation increases, the lateral rigidity increases and this increase intensifies as the $\frac{H}{B}$ ratio is reduced.

The additional deformation of the tire due to the action of the lateral force may be estimated from equation (130) where $dG_w$ represents the sum of the external force and the radial force acting on an element of the girdle ring. The radial component from the girdle ring may be expressed by the equation

$$dG_{w0} = p_w\left(1 - \frac{b}{b_t}\right)\left[b_t - H \cot\sqrt{6\left(1 - \frac{H}{l_s}\right)}\right]dl. \qquad (135)$$

The external force $dG_w'$ may be obtained from the solution of equations (130) and (135), assuming $dG_w' = dG_w - dG_{w0}$ and $b = \frac{dG_w}{p_w dl}$:

$$dG_w' = p_w\, b_t\left[1 - \frac{(H - \delta)\cot\sqrt{6\left(1 - \frac{\sqrt{(H - \delta)^2 + \lambda_s^2}}{l_s}\right)}}{H \cot\sqrt{6\left(1 - \frac{H}{l_s}\right)}}\right].$$

The vertical load

$$G_w = 2\int_0^l dG_w'\, dl$$

or approximately

$$G_w = K_3\,(p_w + K_t)\,\sqrt{D\delta b_t}\left[1 - \frac{(H - \delta)\cot\sqrt{6\left(1 - \frac{\sqrt{(H - \delta)^2 + \lambda_s^2}}{l_s}\right)}}{H \cot\sqrt{6\left(1 - \frac{H}{l_s}\right)}}\right].$$

$$(136)$$

Depending upon force $P_s$, the value of $\lambda_s$ is determined from equation (134). When $\lambda_s \leqslant 0.3\ (H-\delta)$, the effect of the lateral force on the radial deformation may be neglected.

The resistance of a tire to lateral drift is governed not only by its lateral rigidity but also by the length of contact between the tire and the road, the displacement of the rim with respect to the longitudinal plane at the midsection and the slip of the tire element at the contact zone.

Consider a case where there is no slip at the contact zone. It can be assumed that at the point at which the tire comes into contact with the supporting surface, its element does not suffer any lateral displacement. In the present case, the shape of the diagram, representing lateral deformations of the tire under steady state conditions with drift, would be represented by a triangle.

If it is assumed that the lateral deformation of each element is proportional to the lateral force (permissible for $\lambda_s \leqslant 0.25\ H$), then the angle of lateral drift may be expressed in terms of the lateral deformation of the tire at the middle of the contact zone

$$\delta_{\text{drift}} \approx \tan \delta_{\text{drift}} = \frac{\lambda_s}{R \sin \alpha_1}.$$

Substituting the value of $\lambda_s$ from equation (133) in the above expression and taking the coefficient of resistance to drift

$$k' = \frac{P_s}{\delta_{\text{drift}}},$$

we have

$$k' = R^2 \sin \alpha_1\ 2\ a_s\ p_w \left[ \frac{0.375\ l_s}{\sqrt{R^2 - A^2}}\ u_I\ \frac{R - A \cos \alpha_1 + \sqrt{R^2 - A^2} \sin \alpha_1}{1.1\ l_s - H} - 0.8\ \alpha_1 \right].$$

$$(137)$$

From an analysis of the expression for the coefficient $k'$, the results show that it is proportional to the pressure of air inflation in the tire, which progressively increases with an increase in the outer diameter of the tire and decreases with an increase of the difference $(l_s - H)$. Quantity $(l_s - H)$ increases with an increase in the curvature of the sidewalls as well as an increase in the height of the profile which, however, is true only when $\dfrac{H}{l_s} = \text{const.}$

The curve representing the variation of $k'$ as a function of the contact angle $\alpha_1$ and, correspondingly, as a function of the radial deformation of the tire has a maximum. The optimum value of the radial deformation is one that corresponds to the maximum for the coefficient $k'$.

Thus, as a result of the study of the tire profile shape, one may observe the following:

1. A change in the shape of the tire profile has a significant influence on the wheel's basic performance parameters.

2. One may increase the contact area, while keeping the volume occupied by the tire at a constant value, by reducing the relative height $\frac{H}{B}$ of the profile up to 0.5. However, due to the bending of the walls, the permissible radial deformation and, consequently, the multipurpose utility of the tire suffers a decrease.

3. An increase of the curvature of the sidewalls leads to an increase in the permissible radial deformation because of the bending of the sidewalls. However, the lateral rigidity of the tire is significantly reduced.

4. Increasing the magnitude of the differences $(B_F - b_t)$ with $b_t = \text{const.}$ increases the lateral and radial rigidity of the tire; but at the same time, it reduces the permissible radial deformation.

The shape of the profile has a conflicting effect on the various performance parameters. Hence, a solution based on a choice of the optimal parameters of the profile would, at best, be a compromise based on the actual conditions under which a tire is used.

## EFFECT OF TREAD DESIGN

The performance parameters of the wheel are influenced to a significant extent by the following tread parameters:

relative width $\frac{b_t}{B}$;

radius of curvature $r_t$;

tread saturation coefficient $m$;

the outline of the tread (dimensions and shape of cleats and indentations).

The influence of these parameters is diverse in nature depending upon ground-soil conditions.

### Motion on a Paved Road

While selecting the parameters of tire treads, all attempts have been made to provide a reliable grip—both in the longitudinal and lateral directions as well as ensure low internal frictional losses, a minimum pressure exerted by the tire on the road to reduce the wear of the tread and road surface and a noiseless operation of the wheel. When the tread width is made larger, the pressure exerted on the road decreases; but at the same time, the thickness of the tread at the edges of the footprint $\Delta_s$ increases. This, in turn, increases the internal frictional losses, the temperature and the danger of rupture in this zone. The rigidity of the sidewalls and the stresses in the carcass are also augmented. In view of the uncertain effect of the tread width on the various parameters, it is usual to select a compromise value for $b_t$ in the range of

(0.7–0.95) B. The larger values are characteristic for tire treads which have an extremely rugged pattern.

When the curvature of the wheel track is reduced to a specific value, the pressure exerted on the road, the rolling losses and the tread wear also reduce. This is due to a decrease in the deformation of the tire elements and their slip relative to the road, which is caused by the spreading of the spherical crown of the tire into a flat one. The disadvantages in reducing the tread curvature arise mostly from the difference between the radius of curvature of the carcass at the tread zone and the track. This can lead to overloading at the shoulders of the tire and an increase in the nonuniform pressure distribution over the width of the tread for large tire deformations.

For ordinary automobile tires, the optimum value of the curvature of the track has been established from practical experience of many years. The crown of the treadband is 4 to 8% of the profile width [20]. The larger values correspond to tires with a wide track. During operation, the tire tread wears out in such a way that the curvature of the treadband strives to attain the optimal value.

Increasing the saturation coefficient $m$ of the tire leads to a fall in the pressure exerted on the road surface and a reduction in tread wear. However, in such a case, the grip between the wheel and a wet or soiled surface worsens. The optimum value of $m$ established from practical experience lies between $m = 0.6$ and $0.8$.

When the height of cleats or studs is increased, the durability of the tread and its grip on dirt roads improve. However, this is accompanied by greater rolling losses and a higher mass and moment of inertia for the tires. An increase in the rolling losses brought about by increasing the height of the cleats and studs is due to the higher hysteresis losses in the rubber of the treads as well as due to an increase in the slip between the cleats and studs and the road surface. Present-day automobile tires have cleats and studs whose height varies from 10 to 15 mm for trucks, and 6 to 8 mm for light vehicles.

The tread patterns of tires for road usage are exceptionally diverse. Tread pattern has a significant influence on wheel-soil adhesion on wet, dirt and snow covered roads as well as on the flexibility of the tread, the noiseless working of the wheel and tread wear.

A good grip is achieved on wet roads when all the water is expelled from below the cleats. The expulsion of water depends to a large extent on the width of the cleat, which dictates the path taken by the water on its way out. When the width of the cleats is reduced, heat dissipation improves and the flexibility of the tread increases. However, the reduction in the width of the cleats is restricted by structural strength considerations (chipping). As a rule, the ratio between the width to height ratio of the cleats is less than 2.

To ensure a reliable tire grip on slippery roads, both in the longitudinal and lateral directions, a network of grooves is cut into the treads in both directions. The cleats and lugs are often notched to improve expulsion of water.

Noiseless rolling of the wheel is achieved mainly by using a variable pitch for the tread pattern, thus eliminating the tire's tendency to cling to the road.

Figure 60a shows the tread pattern which is widely used for automobiles plying on roads with a hard top cover.

For winter road conditions, the tread must ensure a reliable grip both in the longitudinal and lateral directions on snow and ice covered roads. Better results are obtained with $m=0.6$ to 0.8 and the use of sharp edged cleats or lugs to ensure penetration into the ice cover. The grooves in the tread pattern must provide a reliable drainage system for the expulsion of water.

Figures 60b and c show two variants of tread pattern for winter use.

Fig. 60. Tread patterns of tires:

a—for hard surface roads; b and c—for winter road conditions.

The first variant shows transverse blocks separated by longitudinal grooves for increasing the lateral grip. The variable pitch of the tread reduces tire noise during running, while the V-shaped metallic implants in the blocks improve the tire grip on ice covered roads.

The second variant is an extremely rugged tread pattern consisting of lugs placed at an angle of 45°. Such a pattern in combination with strong shoulders for the tread provides a good tire grip on close-packed snow. A tire with a rugged pattern is suitable for mixed winter road conditions.

For roads with a frozen ice cover, the best wheel-soil grip is obtained with a tread provided with metallic lugs. These lugs are usually placed at the shoulders of the tire, most often on the inner side. The height of the lugs above the surface of the treadband is 1 to 2 mm. About 90 to 120 lugs are provided on a tire and are arranged in such a way that they do not lie in one plane.

In recent years, asymmetric winter tires have been used extensively. One part of the treadband (usually the outer one) is designed for a dry and moist hard top dressing; while the second part (the inner one) is designed to run over snow and ice.

## Motion over Soft (Surface) Soils

The foremost requirement of a tread for running over soft soils is that it must possess as high an adhesive force as possible in the longitudinal direction with a minimum slippage.

The influence of the tread saturation coefficient $m$ and the pitch of the lugs $t$ on the adhesive strength can be ascertained from equation (88). The influence of the saturation coefficient $m$ of the tread pattern varies according to the relationship between the rubber-soil-specific frictional force $\tau_r$ and the specific shear resistance $\tau$ of the soil. Practical experience has confirmed that when $\tau < \tau_r$, which is characteristic of sandy soils, it is advisable to increase the coefficient $m$. If $\tau_r < \tau$, which is a property of cohesive soils, the coefficient $m$ should be reduced. To illustrate this, one may consider the case of tractor tires running mostly on soft cohesive soils. For such tires, the value of the coefficient $m$ selected is the minimum ($m = 0.15$–$0.20$) and restricted only by the strength considerations of the lugs.

Figure 61 shows the relationship between $P_a$, the adhesive force, as a function of the coefficient $m$ for snow, clay and loam.

The effect of the pitch between the lugs has been studied to a lesser extent, and the data available in scientific literature are highly contradictory. In order to clarify this problem, the author devised special experiments which led to

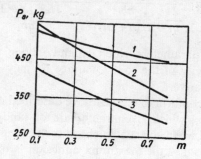

Fig. 61. Relationship between the wheel-soil adhesive force $P_a$ and the saturation coefficient $m$ of the tread.

the following conclusions: on deformable cohesive soils at small slippage, the adhesive force is greater when the pitch $t$ of the lugs is small; while for large values of slippage, the adhesive force increases with an increase of the pitch up to a certain limit. This conclusion has been drawn without taking into account the self-cleaning effect of the tread, which increases with an increase of the lug pitch $t$.

In those cases where the lugs do not entirely penetrate the soil (low pressure, compact soil, long lugs), the soil resistance to shear increases only due to its internal adhesive force. Shear occurs in the form of a sliding fracture at some angle to the horizontal plane. In such a case, increasing the pitch of the lugs leads to a decrease in the adhesive force.

The effect of lug height on wheel-soil adhesion appears to differ depending upon the type and state of the soil. Use of lugs on sandy soils is dangerous since, in this case, the adhesive force due to friction between the rubber and sand particles is greater than that due to ground shear.

The height of the lugs mainly affects the self-cleaning ability of the treads as well as the area of lateral ground shear on cohesive soils, which do not have an adjacent firm layer. With an increase of the height of the lugs, the area of ground shear and, consequently, the tire grip slightly increases. According to M. Bekker, the basic improvement in tire-soil adhesion may be attained by using lugs of a height equal to the width of the tread. However, such a tread construction is impractical.

The height of the lugs has an extremely large influence on tire-soil adhesion on soils which have an adjacent firm base, and on heterogeneous soils, whose compaction increases with depth. It is observed from experience that the lug height is exceptionally effective on muddy roads.

In general, the effect of lug height $\Delta_t$ on the specific adhesive force $\tau_{max}$ may be analytically derived from the expression,

$$\tau_{max} = mq \ \phi_r + (1-m)(q \tan \phi_0 + c_0)(1+C'h^{\mu 1}); \tag{138}$$

$$q = \cfrac{1}{\cfrac{1}{q_s} + \cfrac{ab_t}{E(h+\Delta_t)} \tan^{-1} \cfrac{H_s-(h+\Delta_t)}{ab_t}},$$

where $C'$ and $\mu_1$ are parameters which depend only on the depthwise heterogeneity of the soil. Quantity $C'$ may be either positive or negative.

These equations conform to all the above described considerations. When $c_0 = 0$ and $\tan \phi_0 < \phi_r$, which is characteristic of sandy soil, the maximum adhesion is achieved when the coefficient $m$ tends to unity. When $c_0 > 0$ and $\phi_r < \tan \phi_0$ (cohesive soils), the maximum adhesion is obtained for the coefficient $m$ tending to zero. In such cases, if $C' < 0$ (turf covered soil), it is advisable to use lugs of a small height; while if $C' > 0$, it would be desirable to increase the lug height. The effectiveness of the increasing lug height increases with an increase of $C'$ and $\mu_l$ and decreases with the coefficient $m$.

The effect of the tread saturation coefficient and the lug height is comparatively smaller on the rolling resistance of the soil, which may be estimated from equations (65), (114) and (115).

The shape of the lugs influences the adhesion, self-cleaning ability and flexibility of a tire. Because of the inclination of the supporting surface of the lugs, there is greater compaction of soils between the lugs, resulting in greater ground resistance to shear. When the angle of inclination $\alpha_y$ of the lug bearing surface is excessive, the tire may slip relative to the soil without shearing but by vertical sinkage. In such a case, the tire-soil adhesion may decrease since the internal adhesive force of the soil is not utilized.

The effect of angle $\alpha_y$ on the self-cleaning ability of the tire is ambiguous. On the one hand, for an increase of angle $\alpha_y$, the danger of soil jamming up the space between the lugs decreases; while on the other, the resistance of the lugs to bending increases. Their flexibility relative to the treadband decreases, which in turn decreases their self-cleaning ability.

When angle $\alpha_y$ is sharply increased ($m=$const.), the base of the lugs becomes wider, the rigidity and mass of the tread increase. For high performance off-the-road tires and tractor tires, angle $\alpha_y$ lies between 15 and 30° (average value).

For soft soils, when the values of $m$, $t$ and $\Delta_t$ are fixed, the tread pattern is selected on the basis of its self-cleaning ability and the flexibility of the tread.

Figure 62a, b and c correspondingly show the tread pattern most widely used for tires of automotive vehicles running on soft soils [4]:

*The "continuous herring bone" tread pattern.* Treads with such a pattern are distinguished by their high rigidity and poor self-cleaning ability due to the presence of enclosed recesses and the poor flexibility of the lugs.

*"The open center" ribbed tread pattern.* This tread pattern ensures a high degree of flexibility for the tread together with a better self-cleaning ability than the previous pattern. However, it increases wheel vibrations while running on a hard surface. The arrangement of the lugs at 45° to the longitudinal axis of the tire helps to improve its self-cleaning ability and provides high adhesion in all directions.

*"The curvilinear lug" tread (most recent development).* When lugs are placed at the center of the treadband at a very acute angle, vibrations reduce during the rolling of the wheel on a hard surface and the wear resistance of the tread increases. Treads of such a pattern are in no way inferior compared to those described earlier in their adhesion, flexibility and self-cleaning ability.

A multi-purpose tread for off-the-road vehicles must provide for a high quality of performance, both on prepared automobile roads as well as on diverse types of soil and snow covered surfaces.

The principal requirements of an all-purpose tread are the absence of wheel vibrations while running on a hard surface, low rolling losses on highways, good adhesion under diverse soil surface conditions, good self-cleaning ability, high structural strength and durability under widely varying operating conditions.

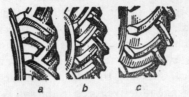

Fig. 62. Tread pattern of tires for use on soft soils.

A continuous belt at the center of the tread-band ensures the vibration free rolling of the wheel. However, this invariably reduces the adhesion on soft soils.

The height of the lugs is decreased to reduce rolling losses on highways and the coefficient of tread saturation is increased to improve its durability. Both these, however, reduce adhesion on soft soils. Naturally an all-purpose tread is not comparable with a tread specially designed for use on roads or for tractors on soft soils. Hence, depending upon the function and proposed conditions of usage, the tread parameters are optimized towards those road conditions which would be most frequently encountered.

Table 7 shows the basic tread parameters of modern tires used on automobiles which have a high degree of off-the-road mobility.

Table 7

| Parameters | Tread | | | |
|---|---|---|---|---|
| | Standard hard road tire | Multi-purpose tire | Off-the-road tire | Tractor tire |
| Saturation coefficient | 0.6–0.8 | 0.5–0.7 | 0.4–0.6 | 0.15–0.3 |
| Height of lugs, mm | 8–15 | 10–20 | 15–25 | 30–60 |
| Width to height ratio of lugs | 1.2–3 | 1.5–3 | 1.5–3 | — |
| Ratio of width of recess $t$ to height of lug $\Delta_t$ | 0.5–0.8 | 0.3–3 | 0.5–4 | — |
| Ratio of width of lugs to their pitch (width of recess) | 2–5 | 2–5 | 0.5–4 | — |
| Angle of inclination of lug walls $\alpha_y$, deg. | 0.5–6 | 0.5–20 | 5–30 | 15–30 |

The first group of tires is designed for use mostly on highways and less so on soil surfaces. These tires are designated as multipurpose tires.

The second group of tires is designed for running mostly on dirt roads and soil surfaces and less frequently on hard top roads. These tires are designated as "off-the-road" or "high mobility" tires.

The tread patterns of off-the-road tires are subdivided into "nondirectional" and "directional" types (Fig. 63).

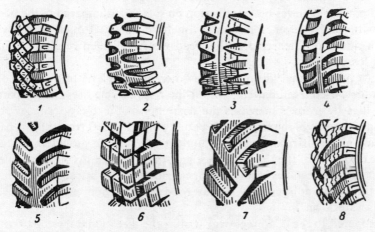

Fig. 63. Tread patterns of "multipurpose" and "off-the-road" tires.

*Nondirectional tread patterns*

1. It combines a "checkerboard pattern" at the center of the treadband with long and sparsely dispersed transverse lugs at the sides. This pattern provides a comparatively high flexibility for the tread, smooth rolling over a hard top road, good adhesion on wet and snow covered roads and a considerably higher adhesion compared to automobile tires. However, it is lower than that for off-the-road tires so far as running on soft soils is concerned.

2. The "straight herringbone" tread pattern is less flexible compared to the previous one, but it provides extremely high adhesion on soft soils in a longitudinal direction. Adhesion in the transverse direction, however, is much lower. The tread has poor self-cleaning ability because of reduced flexibility of the lugs.

3. This pattern consists of triangular lugs separated from each other by longitudinal grooves. It provides high flexibility and better adhesion in the transverse direction.

4. The "semispiral" pattern also has better adhesion in the transverse direction compared to the straight "herringbone" pattern tread. However, a lateral soil reaction component appears in case of such a tread, which adversely affects the stability of the machine.

5. The "herringbone with a continuous belt" at the center of the tread-band is characterized by satisfactory self-cleaning and adhesive properties on soft soils. It ensures a relatively smooth ride over hard covered roads. However, the tread is not sufficiently flexible.

6. The "disjointed herringbone" tread enhances the flexibility, reduces the rolling losses and slightly improves the self-cleaning ability.

7. The "skew herringbone" tread pattern is similar to the tractor tread, except for a considerably larger area for the lugs with a smaller height. Such a tread pattern achieves better adhesion on soft soils compared to the herring-bone pattern. However, for running on hard roads, it does not provide a smooth ride and, furthermore, the tread wear is uneven resulting in higher rolling losses.

8. At present, the "disjointed skew herringbone" pattern is one of the most widely used tread patterns for off-the-road vehicle tires. The separation of the lugs by grooves increases the flexibility of the tread, reduces rolling losses and improves the self-cleaning ability of the tire. Treads of this pattern may have either sharp or rounded shoulders. When the shoulders are rounded, the flexibility of the tire increases, and the pressure distribution over the contact surface becomes highly uniform. However, this leads to a reduction in the transverse adhesion on muddy roads and on soil surfaces whose top layer is waterlogged.

Compared to the nondirectional treads, the directional tread pattern provides better self-cleaning ability and tire-soil adhesion over soft soils—both in the longitudinal and transverse directions, when the tires are mounted in such a way that the vertex is pointed in the direction of rotation. However, when the wheel rotated in the opposite direction, the self-cleaning ability and tire-soil adhesion are adversely affected. Tires with such tread patterns are less suitable for shifting of wheels and utilization of the spare wheel.

## EFFECT OF INFLATION PRESSURE

The air inflation pressure in a tire is one parameter which can be easily altered during operations, depending upon the road-soil surface conditions. Since this parameter appears in all the equations described earlier, one may assess its qualitative effect on the wheel performance parameters.

### Motion on Paved Roads

Decreasing the air inflation pressure $p_w$ leads to a rise in its radial deformation $\delta$ (Fig. 64). This results in a greater tire-soil contact surface, but at the same time increases the coefficient of rolling resistance $f$ heating and tire wear.

Because of the greater tire-soil contact surface $F$, the tire pressure on the road decreases; but there is an increase of slippage of tread elements relative to the road—both in driven and free wheeling conditions. The last named factors have an adverse influence on the road as well as on tread wear. A highly uniform tread wear over its width, which is a minimum in absolute terms, occurs when the deformation of the tire corresponds to that of the entire treadband, spreading out into a plane without overloading the shoulders. The optimum deformation $\delta_{opt}$ for ordinary automobile tires and tires with regulated air inflation lies between $0.11B$ and $0.13B$.

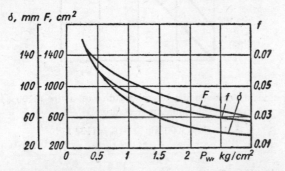

Fig. 64. Influence of air inflation pressure in a tire on performance parameters of a wheel running on a hard road (tire type 12.00–18, $G_w = 1500$ kg).

The effect of pressure at the contact zone on the tire-soil adhesion depends on road conditions. On dry roads, adhesion improves when the inflation pressure is reduced. On muddy roads, this relationship may be reversed due to poor expulsion of the liquid mass from under the lugs at reduced inflation pressures.

The smooth running of an automobile depends to a significant extent on the tire inflation pressure. When the air pressure is reduced, i) the acceleration of the cushioning mass reduces in the high frequency resonance zone, ii) the amplitude of vibrations of the cushioning masses reduces, iii) the probability of tire punctures lessens and iv) the smoothing action of the tire improves. At the same time, the accelerations of the cushioning mass in the low frequency resonance zone increase slightly and the range of road roughness, which results in resonant vibrations of the wheel, becomes larger.

When the inflation pressure is changed, the lateral flexibility and resistance to lateral drift, which have a significant influence on the maneuverability and stability of the vehicle, also change. Figure 65 shows experimental data giving the relationship between the lateral rigidity $\dfrac{P_s}{\lambda_s}$ and the inflation pressure. It may be observed that these relationships agree entirely with equation (134).

The angle of lateral drift depends to a significant extent, not only on tire flexibility but also on the tire-soil contact length and on the adhesion between the tire elements and the soil. When the inflation pressure is reduced, the

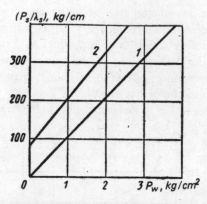

Fig. 65. Relationship between the lateral rigidity of a tire ($1200 \times 500$–$508$) and inflation pressure:

$1$—$G_w = 3000$ kg; $2$—$G_w = 1122$ kg.

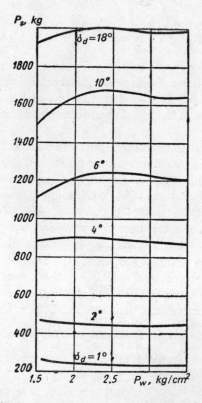

Fig. 66. Relationship between the resistance to lateral drift $P_s$ and inflation pressure ($G_w = 3000$ kg, width $1200 \times 500$–$508$).

deformation of the sidewalls increases; but at the same time, the contact length between the tire and the soil increases and the lateral slip is slightly reduced. Hence, the resistance of the tire to lateral drift $P_s$ is hardly affected by inflation pressure (Fig. 66).

Tangential flexibility is often estimated in terms of the reduction in the rolling radius of the wheel

$$R_w = R_{w0} - \lambda T,$$

where $\lambda$ is the tangential flexibility coefficient.

This is not entirely correct, since the rolling radius depends not only on the tangential elasticity of the tire but also on the skid of the tire elements relative to the road. Skidding occurs at all tangential loads, including the smallest. Since it is extremely difficult to determine slippage and tangential deformation of the tire separately, the effect of inflation pressure $p_w$ on tangential deformation shall be indirectly determined.

Figure 67 shows the experimentally determined relationship $R_w = R_w(T)$ and $\lambda = \lambda(p_w)$ (where $\lambda$ accounts for both the tangential deformation as well as slippage). When the vertical load on the wheel is reduced, $\lambda$ increases which may be only explained as being due to greater slippage. For the maximum vertical load ($G_w = 3160$ kg), the value of $\lambda$ is extremely small (0.005 to 0.015). When the inflation pressure is reduced, the adhesion at the contact zone increases, resulting in a decrease of values of $\lambda$. These tend to zero at very low inflation pressures $p_w$. Consequently, the tangential deformation is so small that its effect on the rolling radius, and, more so, its variation as a function of inflation pressure $p_w$ may be disregarded.

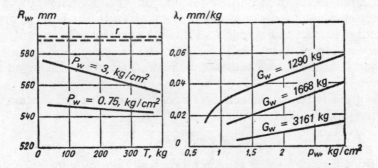

Fig. 67. Effect of inflation pressure on wheel rolling resistance and the tangential flexibility of the tire (tire type: $1200 \times 500$–$508$, $\phi = 0.92$).

## Motion over Soft (Surface) Soils

The effect of inflation pressure on tire deformation and contact surface parameters were discussed earlier in the section on "Wheel–Soil Interaction".

The effect of inflation pressure on rolling resistance is determined by the nature of variation of the soil and tire deformations when pressure $p_w$ is altered. Figure 68 shows the experimentally derived relationship for the principal components of rolling resistance, the ground resistance to rolling $P_{fg}$ and the resistance to rolling due to the energy expended on tire deformation $P_{ft}$ as a function of inflation pressure.

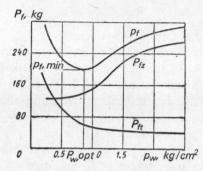

Fig. 68. Dependence of the principal components of wheel rolling resistance as a function of the inflation pressure (tire type 14.00–18; $G_w = 1500$ kg; sandy soil).

Special experiments were carried out on a flat asphalt road to determine functional dependence $P_{ft} = P_{ft} (p_w)$. Data were gathered for $P_{ft}$ as a function of the radial tire deformation $\delta$ and the wheel turning moment $M_w$. Since, for $p_w = \text{const.}$, losses on the internal friction of the tire are governed by the magnitudes of its radial and tangential deformations, it may be assumed that for identical values of these deformations on soft and hard surfaces, the losses due to tire deformation would be identical. On the basis of this assumption, the functional relationship $P_{ft} = P_{ft} (p_w)$ was derived, using the experimental data expressed in form $P_{ft} = P_{ft} (\delta, M_w)$ for a tire running on a hard road and from the known values of $\delta$ and $M_w$ for a wheel rolling on sandy soil.

The force $P_{fg}$ is determined by subtracting the tire deformation losses from the total losses as

$$P_{fg} = P_f - P_{ft}.$$

This is possible for a sandy soil since practically no soil adheres to the tire surface nor is there any tire-soil slippage over the sand.

The relationship between the total rolling resistance $P_f$ and the inflation pressure becomes complicated, acquiring a minimum because of the contradictory nature of the curves $P_{fg} = P_{fg} (p_w)$ and $P_{ft} = P_{ft} (p_w)$.

Figure 69 shows the functional relationship $f = f (p_w)$ for various types of soils and different types of tires. The nature of the function $f = f (p_w)$ for all tires, including ribbed and pneumatic-tired rollers, is the same. On roads having a waterlogged top layer overlying a solid base, the value of $f$ hardly decreases when the inflation pressure $p_w$ is reduced. On the other hand, in certain cases, it increases due to an increase in the width of the ruts formed by the wheels.

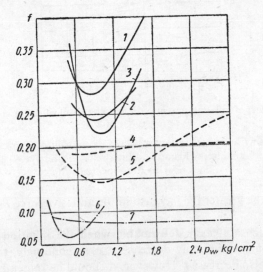

Fig. 69. Dependence of the wheel rolling resistance on inflation pressure in a tire on various types of soils:

1—dry sand; 2—granular snow ($H_s$=30 to 35 cm); 3—plowed loamy soil ($w$=17 to 23%); 4—plowed heavy loam ($w$=30 to 40%, $H_s$=25 cm, $G_w$=1000 kg); 5—loose wet sand ($w$=8 to 10%, $H_s$=35 cm, $G_w$=1500 kg); 6—sand; 7—muddy dirt road. Full lines refer to tire type 1140–700; broken lines refer to tire type 12.00–48; the dotted broken lines refer to tire type 1000 × 1000 × 250; and thick dotted broken lines refer to tire type 16.00–20.

Function $P_f = P_f(p_w)$ may be ascertained analytically from equations (97) and (100). The optimum value of pressure $p_w$ may be obtained from these expressions. The optimal value of inflation pressure in tires increases with an increase in the vertical load on the wheel, the modulus of soil deformation and the hysteresis loss in the tire. When the dimensions of the tire and the thickness of the deformed soil layer increase, the optimal value of inflation pressure $p_w$ decreases.

The consolidated experimental data on the effect of inflation pressure on the tire-soil adhesion coefficient $\phi$ are shown in Fig. 70.

The effect of inflation pressure on tire-soil adhesion becomes evident through the variation of contact parameters. On soils which are homogeneous depthwise, the contact area $F$ appears to be decisive. In less deforming soils the area $F$ increases with a decrease in the pressure $p_w$. In this case, the variation of adhesion is governed by the soil cohesiveness $c_0$. The greater

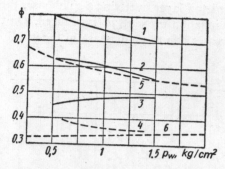

Fig. 70. Effect of inflation pressure on the wheel-soil adhesion coefficient on
various types of soils:

1—plowed loamy soils; 2—dry sand; 3—wet clayey soil; 4—snow; 5—wet loose
sand; 6—waterlogged heavy loam. Full lines refer to tire type 1140–700; broken
lines refer to tire type 12.00–18.

the value of $c_0$, the greater the increase in the adhesive force $P_a$ for an increase
in area $F$.

On soils which are easily deformable when the inflation pressure $p_w$ is
reduced, the contact area may decrease. Correspondingly, the shear resistance of the soil also decreases. However, it should be remembered that when
the pressure $p_w$ is reduced, the area of the flat zone in the contact patch increases, after which the zone of reversed curvature appears. This leads to an
improvement in soil compaction, which is helpful in increasing adhesion and
is very clearly exhibited on sandy soils (curve 5).

On soils which are not depthwise homogeneous in terms of their cohesive
properties, the decisive factor is the nature of variation of the soil along its
depth. Very frequently one encounters soils which have a waterlogged top
layer with a very dry and hard underlying layer. On such soils, a decrease of
pressure $p_w$ often leads to a decrease in adhesion (curve 6).

In the case of wet turf covered soils, the adhesive properties of the top
layer are better than those of the underlying ones. Under these conditions,
when the turf cover is ruptured, adhesion reduces sharply and, hence, it is
advisable to select the inflation pressure based on the load bearing properties
of the turf cover.

The dependence of wheel performance parameters on the inflation pressure analytically obtained for various types of soils is shown in Fig. 71. One
may draw the following conclusion from these results:

In most cases, the sinkage parameter $P_s$ increases slightly with a decrease
in inflation pressure. Only when $P_s$ is close to unity does the influence of inflation pressure become significant;

The traction coefficient $\phi_T$, which characterizes mobility, increases considerably with a decrease of pressure $p_w$ on almost all types of soils. In the

examples considered here, off-the-road mobility on plowed land is achieved only when $p_w < 0.95$ kg/cm²; while on severely waterlogged virgin lands, $p_w < 2.4$ kg/cm².

The traction-efficiency characteristics for various values of $p_w$ have been cited only for a muddy dirt road. These characteristics clearly show that the efficiency factor is highest when $p_w = 1.5$ kg/cm² at all operating conditions. At minimum inflation pressures ($p_w = 0.5$ kg/cm²), the efficiency factor is lower by nearly 70% and the gain in maximum possible traction is 10% greater than for $p_w = 1.5$ kg/cm². The shaded area of the graph indicates the unstable region of motion.

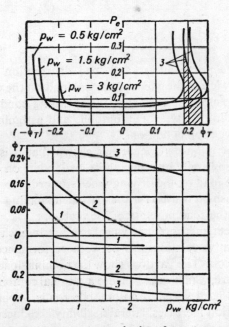

Fig. 71. Effect of inflation pressure on wheel performance parameters (tire type 12.00–18, $G_w = 1500$ kg):

1—plowed land; 2—swampy meadows; 3—muddy dirt road (see Table 16 for soil parameters).

From the known values of $P_e$, $\phi_T$ and power $N_w$ applied at the wheel, one may obtain an expression for the maximum possible speed in terms of traction as follows:

$$v_w = \frac{N_w}{G_w\,(\phi_T + P_e)}.$$

However, it should be noted that the permissible speed is also restricted by the heating up of the tire, which depends upon its deformation and hysteresis properties. Hence, the permissible speed derived from the considerations of tire heating is km/h

$$v_{per} = \left[ \frac{K_t D (B+H) (t_t - t_a)}{P_{ft}} \right]^{3/2}, \tag{139}$$

where $K_t$ is a coefficient;

$t_t$ and $t_a$ are the temperatures of the tire and surrounding air, in degrees celsius.

Thus, even while selecting the optimal value of $p_w$, one must accept a compromise solution in order to ensure the high values of $\phi_T$, $v_{per}$ and minimum $P_e$.

## EFFECT OF VERTICAL LOAD

While selecting the prime mover and load distribution on the axles, the designer must be aware of the effect of vertical load on the wheel performance parameters. This is closely linked with the operating conditions of the automobile, while deciding the type of automobile and assigning its load carrying capacity for the given soil conditions.

Automobile operation experience has shown that it is possible to run a vehicle on certain soils only by reducing its load; while on others, it is advisable to increase the load on the driving wheels in order to increase adhesion. Presently, an air cushion is used for the partial unloading of the wheel so as to improve the off-the-road mobility of the vehicle.

In order to select the optimum wheel loading in each specific case, one must have quantitative relationships between performance parameters and the load on the wheels. Tire catalogs show the nominal load carrying capacity and inflation pressure, which would ensure a rational combination of performance properties on hard surfaced automobile roads. Apart from this, when the radial deformation increases, lateral flexibility is reduced, and the steering control of the automobile worsens.

When the load is simultaneously increased with an increase of inflation pressure as well as stresses in the carcass and the tread rubber, the useful life of the tires is greatly reduced.

When the load is reduced, the coefficient of rolling resistance decreases. Because of smaller radial deformation, the tread wear becomes uneven (greater wear in the central portion). Hence, when reduction of the load becomes unavoidable, it is advisable to reduce the inflation pressure to reestablish optimal radial deformation $\left( \frac{\delta}{H} = 0.11 - 0.13 \right)$.

The optimal load carrying capacity of tires on soil surfaces varies with their mechanical properties since it is restricted, not only by the maximum permissible tire deformation, but also by the load bearing capacity of the soil.

It has been explained earlier that there is less tire deformation on soft soils than on hard surfaces. Hence, depending upon the practical life of a tire on soft soils, the wheel load may be increased.

With an increase of $G_w$, rolling resistance increases in all cases since both tire and soil deformations also increase. However, the decisive factor here is the increase in soil deformation. Almost all the energy expended on soil deformation is irrecoverable, whereas a large part of the energy absorbed in tire deformation can be recovered. Since soil deformation is largely governed by the relationship between the pressure exerted at the contact zone and the load bearing capacity of the soil, the influence of the load on the depth of the ruts becomes greater as the pressure exerted approaches the load bearing capacity.

If $p_w = \text{const.}$, the radial deformation increases with an increase of load, resulting in a greater pressure being exerted on the soil. The relationship between pressure and tire deformation depends on the construction of the tire, particularly on the flexibility of its walls. The greater the flexibility of the walls, the smaller the change in pressure exerted on the soil depending upon the tire deformation. However, this increases the tire-soil contact area.

Change in the contact area also affects soil deformation. However, this effect is weaker compared to that of pressure and is by nature different for different soils. For instance, when the contact width is increased from 25 to 30 cm on a sandy soil, its deformation reduces. Hence, on friable sandy soils, when the load on tires with highly flexible walls is increased, the rut depth undergoes very little change. An increase of load leads to a severe increase of rut depth in the case of soft-plastic clayey soils.

The sinkage of the wheel into the soil is restricted when the soil has a hard underlying layer. An increase of load on tires leads mostly to an increase in their deformation.

Figure 72 shows the effect of vertical load on the depth of ruts for several types of soils. In all these cases, tire deformation is at the maximum permissible limit. This is achieved by increasing the inflation pressure with an increase of load. As can be seen from Fig. 72, the value of $p_w$ corresponding to $\delta_{max}$ depends upon soil properties. The large values of $p_w$ over sandy soils may be explained by the highly uneven pressure distribution at the contact surface due to soil displacement.

Correspondingly the rolling resistance increases with an increase in the depth of the ruts formed by the wheels. In those cases where an increase of $h$ as a function of $G_w$ is arrested, the coefficient of rolling resistance may reduce with the increasing load. This is characteristic of dry arable lands.

The tire-soil adhesive force always increases with an increase of the vertical load. However, in such a case the adhesion coefficient may either increase or decrease. The decisive factor here is the change in the cohesive properties of the soil with its depth. The adhesion coefficient increases with an increase of load $G_w$ on soils whose cohesive properties increase with depth.

116

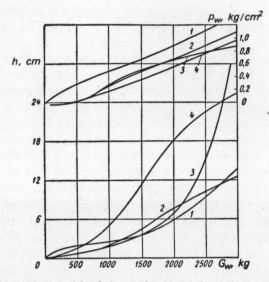

Fig. 72. Effect of vertical load $G_w$ on the depth of ruts $h$ (tire type 12.00–18, $\delta_{max} = 9.8$ cm):

1—sand; 2—muddy dirt road; 3—waterlogged meadow; 4—plowed loamy soil.

In the case of soils which have homogeneous cohesive properties along their depth, the adhesion coefficient most often decreases with an increase of load, since the contact area increases at a slower rate than the load.

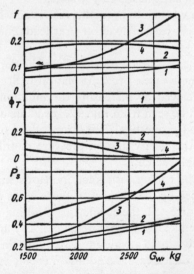

Fig. 73. Effect of vertical load on performance parameters of a wheel (tire type 12.00–18, $\delta = 9.8$ cm, for soil parameters see Table 16):

1—sand; 2—muddy dirt road; 3—waterlogged meadow; 4—plowed loamy soil.

The influence of the vertical load on the performance properties of the wheel is shown in Fig. 73. When the vertical load on the wheels is increased, all the performance parameters progressively worsen for operations on water-logged meadows. For loads $G_w$ exceeding 2500 kg, it becomes impossible to initiate rolling.

On sands and muddy dirt roads, the traction coefficient $\phi_T$ and the coefficient of rolling resistance $f$ hardly change. The sinkage parameter $P_s$ increases considerably with an increase of vertical load. The traction coefficient and the coefficient of rolling resistance worsen with the increase of a vertical load up to 2500 kg on plowed fields and, thereafter, improve with the increasing load. On such soils, it is advisable to choose the vertical load on the basis of the permissible radial deformation of the tire.

# A COMPARATIVE STUDY OF THE PERFORMANCE OF VARIOUS TYPES OF TIRES

## Variable Inflation Tires

Variable inflation tires (Fig. 74) have a profile shape which is similar to the usual automobile tire: $\frac{B_F}{B}=0.7-0.8$ and $\frac{H}{B}=0.9-1.0$. The essential difference between them and the usual automobile tire consists of the fact that they may be operated for short durations at relative radial deformations of $\frac{\delta_{max}}{H}=0.35$. The operation of such tires at even larger radial deformations is restricted by the loss of lateral stability.

Decreasing the minimum inflation pressure, which is helpful in reducing pressure $q_{min}$ on the soil, inevitably leads to an increase in the dimensions of

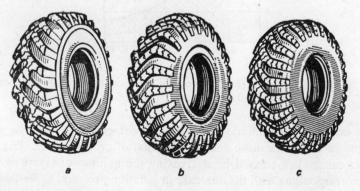

Fig. 74. Variable inflation tires:

a—type 12.00–18, model I-111, type 13.00–18, model I-112, type 14.00–18, model I-113; b—type 12.00–18, model I-150A; c—type 16.00–20, model I-156, type 18.00–24, model I-170.

the profile and the outer diameter (Fig. 75). A reduction in the pressure variation range exerted on the soil through variation of tire inflation (Fig. 76) also occurs. Modern variable inflation tires have a profile which is 25 to 40% larger than for the usual tires of the same load carrying capacity.

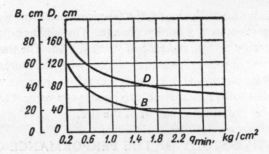

Fig. 75. Dependence of tire dimensions on minimum pressure at the contact zone ($G_w$=1500 kg, $\frac{\delta}{B}$=0.35, $d$=46 cm).

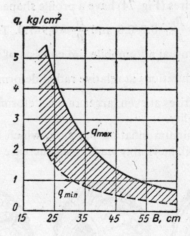

Fig. 76. Dependence of the range of pressure variation at the contact zone on the width of a circular tire profile ($G_w$=1500 kg, $d$=46 cm).

The use of variable inflation tires at large deformations becomes possible when the carcass is far more flexible than that of ordinary tires. The flexibility of a carcass is increased by decreasing the number of layers of the tire cords, corresponding with the decrease in inflation pressure, as well as by the use of extremely tough and flexible materials. However, the greater flexibility of the carcass and higher tire deformation also lead to higher internal friction losses with a corresponding occurrence of the tire heating up [see equation (139)]. Hence, when inflation pressure is reduced, the permissible speed of the vehicle is restricted to a lower value. The permissible speed of vehicles fitted with 12.00–18 and 13.00–18 tires is given below:

| $p_w$, kg/cm$^2$ | 0.5 | 0.5–1 | 1–1.5 | 1.5–2.0 | 2.0–2.5 |
|---|---|---|---|---|---|
| $v_{per}$, km/h | 20 | 20–30 | 30–50 | 50–60 | 60–80 |

Table 8 shows comparative data for variable inflation tires with identical load carrying capacities.

When used on hard surface roads, variable inflation tires are found to be slightly inferior to ordinary tires in their performance.

Variable inflation tires are mounted on split rims with a spacer ring, which is quite intricate and also much heavier than the usual flat wheel rims. The effort involved in assembling and dismantling the wheel is considerably greater than for normal tires.

**Table 8**

| | Load $G_w$, kg | | |
|---|---|---|---|
| | 700–750 | 1550–1600 | 2400–2450 |
| *Variable inflation tires* | | | |
| D–B (B–d) | 886–244 | 1080–330 | 1360–435 |
| | (9.00–16) | (12.00–18) | (16.00–20) |
| Number of plies | 6 | 8 | 12 |
| Mass, kg | 32 | 72 | 130 |
| Inflation pressure, kg/cm$^2$ | 2.5–0.5 | 3.5–0.5 | 1.75–0.5 |
| *Normal tires* | | | |
| D–B (B–d) | 860–175 | 996–253 | 1123–313 |
| | (6.5–20) | (9.75–18) | (12.00–20) |
| Number of plies | 8 | 12–14 | 14–16 |
| Mass, kg | 26 | 65 | 90 |
| Inflation pressure, kg/cm$^2$ | 3.5 | 4.5 | 5.5 |

When a variable inflation tire is fitted to an automobile, both the mass and the moment of inertia of the wheel increase (Table 9) which slightly reduces the dynamic performance of the machine.

On dirt tracks and unprepared terrain, the performance of variable inflation tires is far superior to ordinary tires.

Figure 77 shows the generalized experimental data for rolling resistance and the tractive effort at the hook of the machines fitted with variable inflation tires for running on various types of soils. These data agree with the

Table 9

| | Load $G_w$, kg | |
|---|---|---|
| | 1550–1600 | 2400–2500 |
| *Variable inflation tires with wheel* | | |
| Size of tire | 12.00–18 | 14.00–20 |
| Model | I-111 | I-178 |
| Mass of wheel, kg | 116.45 | 178.6 |
| Moment of inertia, kg·m·sec² | 1.587 | 3.188 |
| *Normal tires with wheel* | | |
| Size of tire | 9.75–18 | 12.00–20 |
| Model | Ya-42 | V-21 |
| Mass of wheel, kg | 99.5 | 133.35 |
| Moment of inertia, kg·m·sec² | 1.183 | 2.105 |

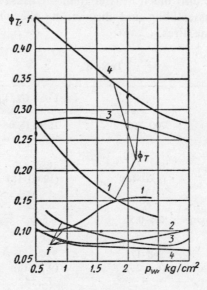

Fig. 77. Performance parameters of passenger car ZIL-157 equipped with variable inflation tires [33]:

1—snow, $H_s$=40 cm; 2—wet sand; 3—muddy dirt road, $H_s$=9–10 cm; 4—meadow.

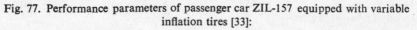

analytical expressions presented earlier. Theoretical and experimental investigations show that variable inflation tires can be used as an effective means of improving the off-the-road mobility of a machine over soft soils.

**Ribbed Tires**

Ribbed tires (Fig. 78) are distinguished by the spherical shape of their profile, which resembles an arch. They have $\frac{B_F}{B}=1$ and $\frac{H}{B}=0.3$–$0.4$. The walls in the zones adjacent to the beading are not very flexible because of the high flexural rigidity. Hence, at large radial deformations, the tread band deforms akin to a membrane "inserted" into the tire. In such a case, the pressure distribution over the contact surface sharply changes. It decreases at the center and increases at the edges of the contact zone. This type of deformation on soft soils ensures the low sinkage of the tire into the soil resulting in improved compaction and low lateral displacement. The membrane type of deformation is not desirable for running on hard roads since it causes high tread wear.

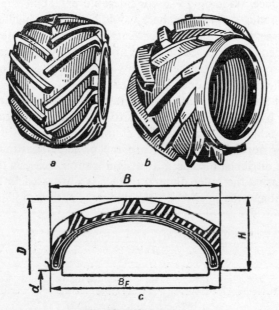

Fig. 78. Ribbed tires:
a—1000–650, I-182; b—1140–700, Ya-146; c—tire profile.

The high tread wear of ribbed tires is caused not only because of uneven pressure distribution over the contact width but, to a much greater extent, due to the skidding of tire elements relative to the soil. This may be explained by the fact that the outer diameter of the tire varies over its width, decreasing from the center of the tire to the sides. Since while rolling, all the longitudinal sections of the tire travel the same distance and execute the same number of revolutions, skidding or tangential deformation opposite to the direction of travel (in the central zone and in the direction of travel at the sides) becomes inevitable. This slippage or tangential deformation, which cause tread wear, are proportional to the difference between the radii of the longitudinal sections of the tire coming in contact with the road.

In the case of ribbed tires, this difference is practically equal to radial deformation since the deflection of their sidewalls is very small. For tires of a circular profile, the major part of the radial deformation is due to deflection of the sidewalls. The difference in the radii of the longitudinal sections, coming into contact with the soil, is much smaller than the radial deformation. Hence, with all other conditions being equal and for identical radial deformations on hard roads, the slippage losses at the contact zone and tread wear of ribbed tires must be greater than those for tires with a circular profile.

To ensure low tread wear on hard roads, it is advisable to reduce the inflation pressure so as to avoid the membrane-like deformation of the treadband and reduce skidding to a considerable extent at the contact zone. Naturally the radial deformation here would be reduced, while the rigidity of the tire increases, having an adverse effect on the smoothness of the ride.

When ribbed tires are used on soft soils, it is advisable to reduce the inflation pressure so as to reduce the pressure exerted on the ground and to make good use of the membrane deformation effect.

Because of the small height to width ratio of their profile, ribbed tires are characterized by a large contact width to radial deformation ratio. Hence for identical radial deformations, the contact area of ribbed tires is much larger than for normal tires. These are the principal advantages of ribbed tires. The use of ribbed tires permits a significant increase in the contact area without increasing the outer diameter. This is illustrated in Table 10 which shows the contact area of ribbed tires and normal tires of identical $D$ and $H$ [68].

**Table 10**

| Tire size | Model | Load, kg | Contact area, cm$^2$ |
|---|---|---|---|
| 1000 × 650 | I-182 | 2000 | 1980 |
| 7.50–20 (2 tires) | M-9 | 2000 | 500 |
| 1140 × 700 | Ya-146 | 3000 | 2000 |
| 260–20 (2 tires) | I-125 | 3100 | 800 |

The contact area of ribbed tires is increased by increasing the width of the wheel.

The specific volume of ribbed tires (referred to a unit contact area) is approximately the same as for variable inflation tires. The specific volume of a wheel fitted with a ribbed tire increases due to the wider wheel rim (Table 11).

The tread construction of a ribbed tire is of extreme importance. When close pitched treads with a high profile saturation coefficient $m$ are used on muddy dirt roads, the tire fails to adhere to the firm underlying soil layer. If the tread pitch is large with long lugs, which are few in number, then good adhesion is obtained on muddy dirt roads and on most of the soft soils. The tire becomes more versatile since a smaller pressure is exerted on the yielding soils due to the large contour area at the contact zone; while on muddy dirt tracks with a hard underlying soil layer, the pressure under the lugs is greater. However, on hard surface roads, the performance of the tire with such treads is unsatisfactory because of vibrations and the rapid wear out tendency of the lugs.

**Table 11**

| Type of tire | Parameter | | | | | | |
|---|---|---|---|---|---|---|---|
| | $\dfrac{m_t}{G_w}$ | $\dfrac{m_w}{G_w}$ | $\dfrac{J_w}{G_w}$ | $\dfrac{V_t}{G_w}$, cm³/kg | $\dfrac{V_w}{G_w}$, cm³/kg | $q_{min}$, kg/cm² | $q_{max}$, kg/cm² |
| Variable inflation | 0.05 | 0.072 | 0.0011 | 200 | 246 | 0.9 | 3.5 |
| Wide profile | 0.028 | 0.054 | — | 150 | 182 | 0.8 | 3.5 |
| Ribbed | 0.037 | 0.072 | 0.001 | 200 | 267 | 0.8 | 2.0 |
| Pneumatic roller | 0.05 | 0.085 | 0.001 | 600 | 630 | 0.3 | 0.8 |

Ribbed tires transform into multipurpose ones when utilizing a compound tread, which is comparatively less rugged, forms a continuous band at the crown and is extremely rugged at the sidewall of the tread band. Such tires ensure vibration free motion with a comparatively low tread wear over hard top roads and a sufficiently high adhesion on soft soils and muddy dirt roads. (They are, however, less effective than tires which have a total rugged tread width.)

The radial rigidity of ribbed tires while running on hard faced roads is close to that of variable inflation tires and normal tires.

The tangential rigidity of ribbed tires on hard surfaced roads is somewhat higher than for variable inflation tires and normal tires.

To reduce the dynamic load during transmission, it is necessary to reduce the tangential rigidity.

The coefficient of change of the rolling radius $\lambda$ for these tires is close to that for normal tires.

## Wide Profile Tires

Wide profile tires (Fig. 79) are manufactured in the USSR based on long range experimental investigations carried out on ribbed tires. The development of wide profile tires was aimed at eliminating certain basic inadequacies that are inherent in ribbed tires while running on hard paved roads as well as to ensure a high quality of tire performance.

The principal difference between wide profile tires and ribbed tires is the highly flexible sidewalls, as in the case of normal tires. Basically they differ from ordinary tires in their greater profile width, rim and tread for identical profile height.

The principal parameter of profile shape is as follows:

$$\frac{H}{B} = 0.55\text{--}0.85; \qquad \frac{B_F}{B} = 0.75\text{--}0.85;$$

$$\frac{b_t}{B} = 0.75\text{--}0.9; \qquad \frac{h_t}{b_t} = 0.08\text{--}0.12;$$

$$\frac{\delta}{H} = 0.14\text{--}0.18.$$

For wide profile tires, the curvature of the tread crown is much smaller than for ribbed tires. Hence, skidding at the contact surface, which results from the differences between the longitudinal radii, is correspondingly less. The membrane-like deformation of the tread does not occur in wide profile tires. All these are helpful in reducing tread wear when running on hard surfaced roads.

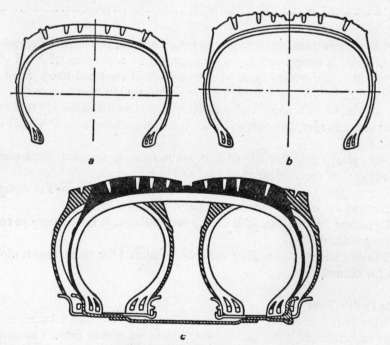

Fig. 79. Wide profile tires:

a—normal tire; b—tire with double tread band; c—comparison of wide profile tire—1100 × 500–508—with normal tires, type 260–20.

The relative mass $\frac{m_t}{G_w}$ is less than that for normal and ribbed tires (see Table 11).

Most of the parameters characterizing the performance of wide profile tires on hard roads are also higher than those of normal and ribbed tires. Their rolling resistance coefficient is almost twice as low as that for ribbed tires and 25 to 30% lower than for the normal tires.

The temperature rise of wide profile tires is less than that of ribbed and normal tires. According to static stand test data, the maximum permissible temperature at the breaker strip of ribbed tires—1140–700 (Ya-170)—was fixed at that corresponding to a speed of 45 kmph, for ordinary tires, 9.00–20 (M-15) at 52 kmph and for wide profile tires, $1200 \times 500$–508 (I-247) at 65 kmph.

At pressures designated for operation on hard roads, the radial rigidity of wide profile tires is slightly higher than that for variable inflation tires and ribbed tires and is closer to normal tires. The tangential rigidity is higher than all other tires. Coefficient $\lambda$ for the variation in the rolling radius, as a function of the torque applied at the wheel, is also less than that of other tires.

Wide profile tires are subdivided into two types:

1. Tires with constant inflation pressure, designated for installation on driving wheels $4 \times 2$ and $6 \times 4$ of automobiles. These tires are superior to ordinary tires in most of the performance parameters, but are inferior to them in reliability and the durability of their beading as well as in the difficulty in mounting and dismounting the tire from the wheel rim. Apart from this, when the wide-profile tires are mounted only on the rear driving wheels it becomes difficult to provide the automobile with spare tires.

2. Variable inflation wide profile tires are designated for use on multiple-drive high off-the-road mobility automobiles. When these tires are used in conjunction with variable inflation circular profile tires, the contact area and the load carrying capacity increase without any change in the outer diameter. Hence, they are primarily used for heavy duty wheels.

**Pneumatic Rollers**

Pneumatic rollers (Fig. 80) exert the lowest pressure on the soil ($q = 0.2$–$0.5$ kg/cm$^2$) compared to other types of tires. This was achieved by considerably increasing the profile width as well as reducing the inner diameter at the rim. This aided in the increase of the profile height. The allowable radial deformation was also correspondingly increased.

Pneumatic rollers are distinguished by their large profile width at relatively moderate outer diameters and very small rim diameters $\left( \frac{B}{D} = 1 - 2; \frac{D}{d} \approx 4 \right)$ compared to other types of tires. The height to width profile ratio for pneu-

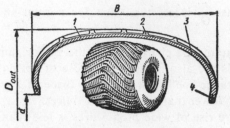

Fig. 80. Pneumatic roller:

1—carcass; 2—tread; 3—hermetic sealing compound; 4—bead.

matic rollers is less than that for other tires $\left(\dfrac{H}{B} = 0.25 - 0.4\right)$. It was earlier explained that for $\dfrac{H}{B} = 0.25 - 0.4$, the contact area and the ratio of radial deformation to profile height $\dfrac{\delta}{H}$ is the largest. However, the length of the profile undergoing unit radial deformation becomes a maximum.

The relative radial deformation of pneumatic rollers is 35% of the profile height. Its relative contact area (per unit volume of the tire) is approximately the same (Table 12) as for variable inflation tires at the maximum permissible deformation. The volume of tire and wheel per unit of load-carrying capacity is greater for pneumatic rollers compared to other tires. The mass of tire and wheel as well as the moment of inertia of the wheel per unit of load carrying capacity for pneumatic rollers does not differ much from those of variable inflation and ribbed tires.

All laws and mathematical equations obtained earlier for pneumatic tires are also applicable to pneumatic rollers.

Both pneumatic rollers as well as other types of tires have rigidity characteristics, which are nonlinear in nature. Rigidity increases as the deformation increases. Pneumatic rollers manufactured in the USSR have a radial rigidity of 10–22 kg/mm, which is 2–5 times lower than that of other types of tires. The curvature of load characteristics slightly increases when the $\dfrac{H}{B}$ ratio is reduced and, hence, it is greater for pneumatic rollers than for other tires (Fig. 81).

The nature of deformation of the tire cord and the rubber in the carcass of pneumatic rollers does not differ from that of ordinary tires [6]. However, the deformation zone spread around the periphery reaches almost 300° (for standard tires, it is 120° and for ribbed tires, nearly 200°). This is explained by the larger width of the profile and the greater crown angle subtended by the cords. The maximum deformation due to compression at the sidewalls is somewhat higher than for ordinary tires (5% instead of 3 to 4%), which shortens the service life of the tires. Deformation of the carcass elements in the tread band of pneumatic rollers is less than that of other tires due to the smaller curvature of the carcass in this zone.

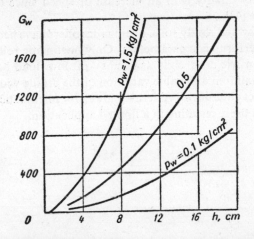

Fig. 81. Loading characteristics of pneumatic rollers 1000 × 1000–250, I-245.

Because of the small circumferential flexibility of the tread band as well as the large radial elasticity, the rolling radius $R_w$ of pneumatic rollers is considerably greater than the dynamic radius $R_d$ (Fig. 82). If in design calculations, the rolling radius is replaced by the dynamic radius, it would lead to a much greater error for pneumatic rollers than for other types of tires.

Membrane-type deformation of the tread band is characteristic of both pneumatic rollers as well as ribbed tires because of the large angle of inclination of the sidewall tire cords to the vertical. This causes an arching effect on soft soils and a rapid tread wear on hard roads. The tread wear increases also

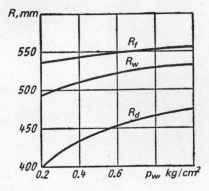

Fig. 82. Comparison of rolling radius $R_w$ with the dynamic radius $R_d$ and free radius $R_f$ (pneumatic roller I-245, $G_w = 1000$ kg, $M_w = 0$).

due to the large height of its arc (for pneumatic rollers, $h_t = 50$–$70$ mm and for variable inflation tires, $h_t = 25$–$40$ mm).

According to investigations on pneumatic rollers, the rolling losses must increase extremely rapidly with an increase of speed since they have a low inflation pressure [43].

On virgin snow and sandy soils, pneumatic rollers have been found to have extremely high performance parameters. Only pneumatic rollers are suitable for operation on yielding soils (swamps) of low load bearing capacity. However, the maximum allowable variation of the profile width and the pressure at the contact zone are considerably lower for pneumatic rollers than for variable inflation tires, resulting in a limited application.

# CHAPTER 4

# Analysis of Multiwheeled and Combined Traction Vehicles

## THE ROLLING OF A WHEEL OVER A SINGLE TRACK

The nature of variation of the mechanical properties of soil due to the consecutive passage of wheels over a single track is of crucial importance in the effective utilization of multiwheeled vehicles. This problem is ultimately connected with the effect of load duration on soil deformation.

According to the experimental results obtained by many investigators, soil deformation due to the consecutive rolling of several wheels may be represented as follows: soils which are devoid of cohesion are subject to rapid deformation; highly cohesive soils deform at a slower rate. The modulus of deformation $E$, the internal adhesion $c_0$ and the load bearing capacity $q_s$ were found to be higher for a rapidly increasing load than for a gradually increasing one. On the contrary, the coefficient of friction tan $\phi_0$ is less for a short duration load compared to a longer one.

Repeated loading, which is characteristic of a consecutive passage of a set of wheels over a single track, prolongs the duration of wheel–soil interaction. The passage of one wheel, in some cases, leads to consolidation of the microstructure of the soil with an increase in its load bearing capacity and modulus of deformation. On the other hand, it can also disrupt the soil structure so that the soil deformation may exceed that of a prolonged load applied on the soil only once.

When a wheel rolls over a soil, the build-up of plastic deformation occurs differently, depending upon its type and composition as well as on the relationship between the pressure exerted on the soil and its load bearing capacity.

It is usually observed that there are four principal cases of possible build-up of plastic deformation when a repeated load is applied to the soil.

1. Being elastic, deformation does not actually increase; the microstructure and the density of the soil remain practically unchanged. This has been observed on cohesive soils with a moisture content less than that for the plastic limit for any possible type of normal loading.

2. The steady increase of deformation following the logarithmic law. This case corresponds to the plastic state of the soil, where the load does not exceed the load bearing capacity.

129

3. Initially, deformation increases in the same manner as in the previous case and, thereafter, in an almost linear fashion (without any damping). This is characteristic of moist soils below the yield limit where the load exceeds the load bearing capacity of the soil.

4. Deformation progressively increases, which corresponds to a moist soil approaching the yield limit or to the action of the load considerably in excess of the load bearing capacity of the soil.

The second and third examples have great practical significance. The first corresponds to hard soil surfaces, while the fourth applies to soils which are almost impossible to traverse.

G.I. Pokrovskii [48] proposed that short duration loads can be taken into account by increasing the dynamic modulus of deformation as follows:

$$E_\mathrm{d} = E\left(1 + \frac{B}{t}\right), \tag{140}$$

where $B$ is a constant depending upon the type of soil;

$t$ is the duration for which the load acts on the soil;

$E$ is the modulus of deformation under static loading.

The values of $E_\mathrm{d}$ and $E$ in equation (140) are determined from the total deformation of the soil, i.e., $E_\mathrm{d} = \frac{q}{h}$.

Substituting for $E_\mathrm{d}$ in equation (140), the expression for the depth of the rut formed by the wheel is

$$h = \frac{q}{E\left(1 + \frac{B}{t}\right)} = \frac{q_\mathrm{d}}{E}.$$

It may be observed from the last expression that the transient nature of the load may be taken into account by replacing the actual pressure $q$ by its dynamic value obtained from the expression

$$q_\mathrm{d} = \frac{q}{1 + \frac{B}{t}}. \tag{141}$$

Expressing the duration for which the load is applied in terms of speed $v$, the number of passes $n$ and contact length $L_\mathrm{w}$, equation (141) transforms to

$$q_\mathrm{d} = \frac{q}{1 + \frac{Bv}{L_\mathrm{w}n}}. \tag{142}$$

After substituting the value of dynamic pressure in the basic expression for soil deformation—equation (13)—we have

$$q = \frac{1 + \dfrac{Bv}{L_w n}}{\dfrac{1}{q_s} + \dfrac{ab}{Eh} \tan^{-1} \dfrac{H_s - h}{ab}}. \tag{143}$$

Constant $B$ is estimated by utilizing the method recommended by N.A. Ul'yanov [63]. He assumed that

$$E_d = E(1 + \Omega \sqrt{v}),$$

where $v < 20$ km/h (5.5 m/sec);

$\Omega = 0.09$–0.11 for cohesive soils;

$\Omega = 0.06$–0.08 for noncohesive soils.

Making a preliminary assumption that $L_w \approx 0.5$ m and $n = 1$, the constant $B$ is obtained as 0.015–0.02 for noncohesive soils and 0.022–0.03 for cohesive soils.

Constant $B$ is, to a large extent, governed by the permeability characteristics of the soil. The higher the permeability, the greater the value of $B$. The permeability of the soil increases with a decrease of clay particles in the soil, for which the internal friction angle $\phi_0$ usually increases. Hence, one may approximate constant $B$ in terms of the friction angle:

$$B = \frac{k}{2\phi_0}, \tag{144}$$

where $\phi_0$ is expressed in degrees; $k \approx 1° \cdot$ sec.

According to equation (144), constant $B$, selected on the basis of data given by N.A. Ul'yanov, corresponds to $\phi_0 = 33$–$25°$ for noncohesive soils and $\phi_0 = 23$–$15°$ for cohesive soils. This corresponds to the values of $\phi_0$ given in Table 2.

If the expression for dynamic pressure $q_d$ is substituted in equation (37), then the effect of speed and number of passes of the wheel on adhesive properties of the soil would be taken into consideration, i.e.,

$$\tau_{max} = \frac{q \tan \phi_0}{1 + \dfrac{Bv}{L_w n}} + c_0 \zeta. \tag{145}$$

Equation (145) holds good for $\dfrac{q}{q_s} \leqslant 0.9$. At $\dfrac{q}{q_s} > 0.9$, constant $B$ should be assumed to be zero.

It follows from equation (145) that when speed increases, adhesion reduces and when the number of wheel passes increases, adhesion increases. This effect is governed by the value of constant $B = \dfrac{k}{2\phi_0}$. It has the largest value for clayey soils and the lowest for sandy soils. All these conclusions coincide with the experimental data.

## EFFECT OF AXLE NUMBER ON VEHICLE PERFORMANCE

In order to analyze the effect of the number of axles on the performance characteristics of automobiles, the following shall be assumed:

The shape of wheel-soil contact area is rectangular $\left(\dfrac{L_w}{b}=v\right)$ and the pressure distribution over the contact surface $q=$ const. for all axles. The width of the contact area shall be expressed in terms of the gravitational force of the automobile $G_a$ and the number of axles is taken to be $N$. Then

$$b=\sqrt{\frac{G_a}{2vNq}}. \tag{146}$$

Based on first estimates, the maximum possible number of passes of the automobile over a single track $n_{max}$, the coefficient of rolling resistance and the traction coefficient shall be assumed.

### Effect of the Axle Number on the Permissible Number of Passes

Equations (20), (143) and (146) are used to obtain a general expression for the maximum possible number of passes of a vehicle over a single track as a function of the gravitational force $G_a$ of the automobile, the permissible depth of rut $h_{per}$, the soil parameters ($X_1$, $X_2$, $E$, $H_s$) and the vehicle parameters ($N$, $v$, $q$):

$$n_{max}=\cfrac{2Bv}{\sqrt{\dfrac{2G_a\,Nv}{q}}\left\{\dfrac{2q}{\pi\left(X_1\sqrt{\dfrac{G_a}{2vNq}}+X_2\right)}\tan^{-1}\dfrac{\pi\,(H_s-h_{per})}{2\sqrt{\dfrac{G_a}{2vNq}}}+\dfrac{a}{Eh_{per}}\sqrt{\dfrac{G_aq}{2vN}}\tan^{-1}\dfrac{H_s-h_{per}}{a\sqrt{\dfrac{G_a}{2vNq}}}-1\right\}} \tag{147}$$

Let us consider some specific cases.

1. Loamy and clayey soils without an adjacent hard soil layer.

Assuming $X_1\approx0$ and $H_s=\infty$, we have

$$n_{max}=\cfrac{2Bv}{\dfrac{\pi aG_a}{2Eh_{per}}+\left(\dfrac{q}{X_2}-1\right)\sqrt{\dfrac{2G_aNv}{q}}}. \tag{148}$$

The function $n_{max}=n_{max}(N)$, as expressed by equation (148), increases for $q<X_2$ and decreases for $q>X_2$. Consequently, when pressure at the contact surface is less than the load bearing capacity of the soil (soil becomes compacted), it is advisable to increase the number of axles. When the pressure is more, the number of axles should be reduced.

2. Sandy soils without an adjacent hard base. Since $X_2 \approx 0$ and $H = \infty$, then

$$n_{max} = \frac{2Bv}{\dfrac{2qvN}{X_1} + \dfrac{\pi a G_a}{2 Eh_{per}} - \sqrt{\dfrac{2 G_a N v}{q}}}. \tag{149}$$

Testing the function $n_{max} = n_{max}(N)$ for maxima, we obtain

$$N_{opt} = \frac{G_a X_1^2}{8 q^3 v}. \tag{150}$$

In most cases, $X_1 < 0.04$; $q > 1$; $v > 1$. Hence, $N_{opt} \leqslant 0.000133 G_a$. For $G_a \leqslant$ 15000 kg, the maximum number of passes is obtained for a two axled vehicle. Three and four axled vehicles can be highly effective on sandy soils only if the gravitational force exerted by the vehicle exceeds 15 tonnes.

3. Loams and clayey soils with an underlying hard base. For this case, $X_1 \approx 0$; $\tan^{-1}(F) \approx (F)$ and, hence,

$$n_{max} = \frac{Bv}{\dfrac{vq(H_s - h_{per})N}{X_2} + \sqrt{\dfrac{G_a Nv}{2q} \left[ \dfrac{q(H_s - h_{per})}{Eh_{per}} - 1 \right]}}. \tag{151}$$

For those cases where $\dfrac{q(H_s - h_{per})}{Eh_{per}} > 1$, the function $n_{max} = n_{max}(N)$ is seen to decrease. The number of passes is found to be a maximum when the number of axles is a minimum.

For the cases which are most likely to occur $\dfrac{q(H_s - h_{per})}{Eh_{per}} < 1$ and the function $n_{max} = n_{max}(N)$ has a maximum so that

$$N_{opt} = \frac{G_a X_2^2}{8 v q^3} \left[ \frac{1}{(H_s - h_{per})} - \frac{q}{Eh_{per.}} \right]^2. \tag{152}$$

4. Sandy soils with an underlying hard base. Since $X_2 \approx 0$ and $\tan^{-1}(F) \approx (F)$, then

$$n_{max} = \frac{Bv}{\dfrac{vq(H_s - h_{per})N}{X_1} \sqrt{\dfrac{2vqN}{G_a}} + \sqrt{\dfrac{G_a Nv}{2q} \left[ \dfrac{q(H_s - h_{per})}{Eh_{per}} - 1 \right]}}; \tag{153}$$

$$N_{opt} = \frac{\left[ 1 - \dfrac{q(H_s - h_{per})}{Eh_{per}} \right] G_a X_1}{6vq(H_s - h_{per})q}. \tag{154}$$

### Effect of the Axle Number on Rolling Resistance

The simplest expression (117) shall be used for determining the coefficient of the rolling resistance of the soil, $f_s$:

$$f_s = \frac{2}{G_a} q_d hb\zeta_z.$$

Writing $\delta = C_0 b$ and substituting for $q_d$, $b$ and $h$ from equations (142), (146) and (117), for a soil without an underlying hard base, we have

$$f_s = \frac{1}{vN} \left\{ \frac{\zeta_z \alpha \left( X_1 \sqrt{\dfrac{G_a q}{2\,vN}} + q X_2 \right)}{E\left[ \left(1 + Bv\sqrt{\dfrac{2qN}{G_a v}}\right)\left(X_1\sqrt{\dfrac{G_a}{2vNq}} + X_2\right) - q \right]} \right\}; \tag{155}$$

for soils with an underlying hard base

$$f_s = \frac{H_s q^2 \zeta_z}{\sqrt{2\,vNq\,G_a}\left(1 + Bv\sqrt{\dfrac{2qN}{G_a v}}\right)^2 \left[ \dfrac{q}{1 + Bv\sqrt{\dfrac{2qN}{G_a v}}} + \sqrt{E\left(X_2 + X_1\sqrt{\dfrac{G_a}{2vNq}}\right)} \right]}. \tag{156}$$

An analysis of equation (155) shows that for $X_1 \approx 0$ (cohesive soils), the coefficient of rolling resistance decreases with an increase in the axle number. For the case when $X_2 \approx 0$ (noncohesive soils), the function $f_s = f_s(N)$ has a maximum and

$$N_{opt} = \frac{2G_a}{9q\left(\dfrac{q\sqrt{v}}{X_1} - \dfrac{Bv}{\sqrt{v}}\right)^2} \approx \frac{2\,G_a\,X_1^2}{9\,vq^3}. \tag{157}$$

According to equation (157), the optimal number of axles, with respect to the coefficient $f_s$, is mainly dependent upon the pressure exerted at the contact surface. On sandy soils at $q > 2$ kg/cm², $N_{opt}$ is almost always less than or equal to 2. At lower pressures, the optimum value of the number of axles with respect to $f_s$ may be greater than two.

For soils which have an underlying firm base, the rolling resistance, according to equation (156), is seen to decrease when the number of axles is increased—irrespective of the cohesive properties of the soil.

## Effect of the Axle Number on Wheel-Soil Adhesion

The coefficient of wheel-soil adhesion can be expressed with the help of equation (117), assuming $\phi = \dfrac{\tau}{q_d}$ and substituting for $q_d$ and $b$ from equations (142) and (146). We then have

$$\phi = \frac{1}{N} \sum_{i=1}^{i=N} \left[ \cfrac{1}{\cfrac{1}{\cfrac{\tan\phi_0\sqrt{G_a v N_i}}{\sqrt{G_a v N_i} + Bv\sqrt{2q}} + \cfrac{c_0}{q}\left(1 - \cfrac{t}{\delta_s}\sqrt{\cfrac{2qN_i}{G_a v}}\right)} + \cfrac{q}{E' q_s}\sqrt{\cfrac{2qN_i}{G_a v}}} \right].$$

(158)

It follows from equation (158) that the maximum value of the coefficient of wheel-soil adhesion increases with the increase in the number of axles, if $B > 0$.

The slippage coefficient $\delta_s$, corresponding to a given value of $\phi$, also increases with an increase of the number of axles except when $\phi \approx \phi_{max}$.

Equations (41) to (43) and (51) to (101) were processed on an electronic computer to obtain a quantitative analysis, where $q$ was substituted by $q_d$ obtained from equation (142).

1. The soil parameters which were assumed for these calculations are shown below.

| Type of soil | Parameters | | | | | | | | |
|---|---|---|---|---|---|---|---|---|---|
| | $v$, g/cm² | $E$, kg/cm² | $H_s$, cm | $\phi_0$, deg | $c_0$, kg/cm² | $\phi_r$ | $E'$, kg/cm² | $E_r'$, kg/cm² | $B$ |
| plowed soil | 1.1 | 5 | 40 | 6 | 0.07 | 0.2 | 5 | 10 | 0.05 |
| virgin soil | 1.2 | 15 | 200 | 3 | 0.2 | 0.2 | 10 | 10 | 0.06 |

2. Tire parameters: $t = 10$ cm; $m = 0.4$; $\varDelta = 2$ cm; $k_t = 0.35$ kg/cm²; $H = B$ varies from 19 to 76 cm; $R = 1.8\ B$; $h_t = 0.1\ B$; $b_t = 0.82\ B$.

3. The gross mass of the automobile is 12000 kg.

Vehicles with one, two, three and four axles have been compared with each other under conditions where the relative radial deformation of the tire is identical for all the vehicles $\left(\dfrac{\delta}{H} = 0.25\right)$ and that the inflation pressure is also identical for all of them.

Figure 83 shows the effect of the number of axles on the principal performance parameters of the vehicle. On plowed fields, which have a firm layer of underlying soil, the depth of the rut formed by the wheels doubles when the number of axles is increased from two to four. The coefficient of rolling resistance remains practically unchanged, while the traction coefficient decreases by 7%. On virgin soils, where the top layer of soft soil is 200 cm thick, an increase of the number of axles leads to contrary results. The depth of the rut reduces significantly (by 30%) with an increase of the axles up to two; however, a further increase in the number of axles, results in only a minor increase. The coefficient of rolling resistance sharply reduces (one

136

axle: $f=0.14$; four axles: $f=0.05$), while the traction coefficient increases by about 13%. For an infinite increase in the number of axles, the depth of the rut and the coefficient of rolling resistance asymptotically approach zero; while the traction coefficient approaches the coefficient of wheel-soil adhesion. The curve showing the relationship between the profile width and number of axles is close to hyperbolic.

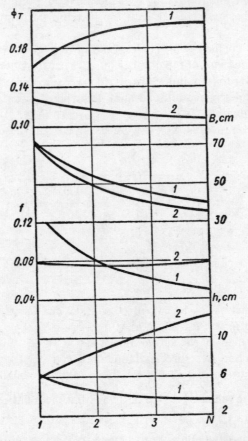

Fig. 83. Effect of the axle number on the performance parameters of the vehicle ($G_a=12000$ kg; $\dfrac{\delta}{H}=0.25$):

1—waterlogged soil; $H=200$ cm, $p_w=0.6$ kg/cm$^2$; 2—plowed land; $H=40$ cm, $p_w=0.8$ kg/cm$^2$.

It is evident from the graph shown in Fig. 83 that for identical pressures, the performance parameters of different types of vehicles are different and their nature of variation as a function of the number of axles is also different. Hence, it is practically impossible to select the parameters of vehicles having a different number of axles in order that their performance parameters could be identical.

In such a case, the depth of the ruts does not have any significance if it is considerably smaller than the clearance of the vehicle.

The most important parameter for the towing vehicle is the traction co-efficient. Figure 84 shows the profile width as a function of the number of axles computed on the basis of the identical traction coefficient ($\phi_T = 0.15$).

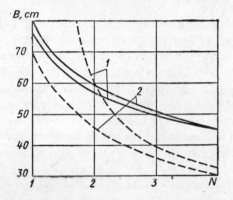

Fig. 84. Effect of the axle number on the width of the tire profile

$$(G_a = 12000 \text{ kg}; \frac{\delta}{H} = 0.25):$$

1—$f$=0.06 (for all the vehicles under comparison); 2—$\phi_T$=0.15 (for all the vehicles under comparison). Full lines represent soil No. 2 and broken lines represent soil No. 3 of Table 16.

A two axled vehicle suitable for plowed fields has a width $B = 59$ cm; while for a four axled vehicle $B = 45$ cm. The total volume of the wheel ($v_w \approx 2\pi RBN$) of a two axled vehicle is 8.5 m³ and that of a four axled one is 7.4 m³.

The total mass of tires for a two axled vehicle is about 1240 kg; while for a four axled one, it is 1170 kg. It may be observed that the total mass of the wheel and the total mass of the tires is slightly on the higher side for a two axled vehicle. Considering the fact that the construction of a two axled machine is far simpler and cheaper than a four axled one, a two axled machine may be prepared as a towing vehicle on plowed fields. If one selects a single axled vehicle (tow vehicle with a single driving axle), then the required tire width becomes 80 cm. The total volume of the wheel then turns out to be 10.5 m³, and the total mass of tires is approximately equal to 1200 kg. In case a single driving axle is used, the total mass of the tow vehicle must be greater than that of a two axled vehicle; since a part of the automobile mass must be applied at the driving wheels. In recent years, there has been a ten-dency to changeover from 4 × 2 to 4 × 4 arrangement tractors.

For operations on virgin soils, a two axled towing vehicle must have a tire width $B=46$ cm; while for a four axled one, $B$ should be equal to 30 cm. The total volume of wheels of a two axled machine is 3.97 m³; whereas that for a four axled one is 2.2 m³. The total mass of the tires of a two axled vehicle equals 700 kg; while it is 480 kg for a four-axled vehicle. At present a four axled vehicle appears to be superior in terms of tire mass and wheel volume. However for a proper selection of the appropriate number of axles there is a need for a more comprehensive analysis of the effect of the axle number.

For machines operating without trailers, the most important parameter is the coefficient of rolling resistance with a sufficient margin available in wheel-soil adhesion. As can be seen from Fig. 84, the tire size for moving on plowed fields with $f=0.06$ hardly varies with the number of axles on the machine for $\phi_T=0.15$. For virgin soils, if one is to provide $f=0.06$ with a reduced number of axles, the tire size has to be sharply increased. For a four axled vehicle, the necessary tire width is $B=37.5$ cm; while for a two axled machine, $B$ should be equal to 60 cm. For a single axled vehicle, the required tire size is extremely unrealistic. The total volume of wheels of a four axled machine comes to 4.28 m³ and that for a two axled one, 8.85 m³. The total mass of tires of a four axled vehicle equals 780 kg and that for a two axled one, 1300 kg. At present, the four axled vehicle appears to be considerably advantageous, both in terms of mass as well as tire size.

## LOAD DISTRIBUTION OVER THE AXLES

### Effect of the Axle Load Distribution on the Depth of the Ruts

In order to make a theoretical analysis of this problem, equation (143) is transformed to obtain $h$:

$$h = \frac{ab \tan^{-1} \dfrac{H_s - h}{ab}}{E \left( \dfrac{1}{q_d} - \dfrac{1}{q_s} \right)}.$$

Equation (143) is applicable for the total number of wheel passes when $L_w=$ const. and $q=$ const. However, in the problem under consideration, $G_w \neq$ const. and consequently, neither $q$ nor $L_w$ are constant. In order to find an expression for $q_d$ for various values of $N$ and variables $q$ and $L_w$, let us first consider the physical nature of soil deformation during the successive passes of the wheel.

*Two axled vehicle.* When a single wheel passes over the soil, the load can be considered to be a gradually increasing one. During the first pass, the soil deforms corresponding to pressure $q_d$ for $n=1$ given by equation (142):

$$q_{d1} = \frac{q}{1 + \dfrac{Bv}{L_w}}. \tag{159}$$

Complete deformation does not occur. During the second pass, if $q$ remains unchanged, the duration for which the load is transmitted increases and, as a consequence, additional soil deformation takes place. The total deformation at the end of the second pass is given by $q_{d2}$ for $n=2$, i.e.

$$q_{d2} = \frac{q}{1 + \dfrac{Bv}{2L_w}}. \tag{160}$$

The apparent specific load corresponding to the second pass is

$$q'_{d2} = \frac{q}{1 + \dfrac{Bv}{2L_w}} - \frac{q}{1 + \dfrac{Bv}{L_w}}. \tag{161}$$

If during repeated passes, the load on the wheel is greater than that of the first pass ($q_2 > q_1$ and $L_2 > L_1$), then the additional soil deformation is greater. In view of the steady nature of the load applied at the wheels, one may assume that when the repeated load is increased up to $q_1$, additional deformation is similar to the first case ($q_2 = q_1$); while if the load is greater ($q_2 > q_1$), the soil deformation spreads to a greater depth. Soil regions, which were untouched, begin to deform and the action of this additional load becomes similar to the load applied during the first pass. It may also be slightly attenuated due to the action of the compacted top layer. This attenuation of the load is estimated by the coefficient

$$K_L = 1 - \left(\frac{q_1}{q_2}\right)^{2n''}.$$

Then

$$q_{d2} = \frac{q_1}{1 + \dfrac{Bv}{2L_{w1}}} + \left(\frac{q_2}{1 + \dfrac{Bv}{L_{w2}}} - \frac{q_1}{1 + \dfrac{Bv}{L_{w1}}}\right) K_L; \tag{162}$$

$$q_{d2} = \frac{q_1}{1 + \dfrac{Bv}{2L_{w1}}} - \frac{q_1}{1 + \dfrac{Bv}{L_{w1}}} + \left(\frac{q_2}{1 + \dfrac{Bv}{L_{w2}}} - \frac{q_1}{1 + \dfrac{Bv}{L_{w1}}}\right) K_L. \tag{163}$$

If during repeated passes, $q_2 < q_1$ and $L_{w2} < L_{w1}$, additional deformation proceeds as in the first case, but up to a lower value than

$$q_{d2} = \left(\frac{q_1}{1 + \dfrac{Bv}{2L_{w1}}} - \frac{q_1}{1 + \dfrac{Bv}{L_{w1}}}\right) \frac{q_2\left(1 + \dfrac{Bv}{L_{w1}}\right)}{q_1\left(1 + \dfrac{Bv}{L_{w2}}\right)}; \tag{164}$$

$$q_{d2} = \frac{q_1 L_{w1}}{L_{w1} + Bv} + \frac{q_2 L_{w2} Bv}{(2L_{w2} + Bv)(L_{w2} + Bv)}. \tag{165}$$

Expressing $q$ and $L_w$ in terms of load $G_w$, using the relationships:

$$G_w = \frac{\pi}{4}(p_w + k_t)\,bL_w; \quad b = \frac{qb_t}{p_w + k_t}; \quad L_w = vb,$$

we have $L_w = A_2\sqrt{G_w}$; $q = A_1\sqrt{G_w}$;

where $A_2 = \sqrt{\dfrac{4\,v}{\pi\,(p_w + k_t)}}$; $\quad A_1 = \sqrt{\dfrac{4\,(p_w + k_t)}{\pi v b_t^2}}$.

These are substituted in the expression for $q_{d2}$.

1. When $G_{w1} = G_{w2}$, then from equation (160),

$$q_{d2} = \frac{2A_1\,A_2\,G_w}{2A_2\sqrt{G_w} + Bv}. \tag{166}$$

2. When $G_{w1} < G_{w2}$, then, according to equation (162),

$$q_{d2} = A_1\,A_2\,G_{w\,av}\left[\frac{2 - W_1}{A_2\sqrt{(2 - W_1)\,G_{w\,av}} + Bv} - \frac{W_1}{A_2\sqrt{W_1\,G_{w\,av}} + Bv}\right.$$

$$\left. + \frac{2W_1}{2A_2\sqrt{W_1\,G_{w\,av}} + Bv}\right], \tag{167}$$

where $W_1 = \dfrac{G_{w1}}{G_{w\,av}}$;

$G_{w\,av}$ is the average load applied at the wheel when the gravitational force is uniformly distributed.

3. When $G_{w1} > G_{w2}$ then from equation (165),

$$q_{d2} = A_1\,A_2\,G_{w\,av}\left[\frac{2 - W_1}{A_2\sqrt{(2 - W_1)\,G_{w\,av}} + Bv}\left(\frac{Bv}{2A_2\sqrt{W_1\,G_{w\,av}} + Bv}\right)\right.$$

$$\left. + \frac{W_1}{A_2\sqrt{W_1\,G_{w\,av}} + Bv}\right]. \tag{168}$$

Figure 85 shows the functional relationships $q_{d2} = q_{d2}\,(W_1)$ and $q_{d1} = q_{d1}\,(W_1)$ for the following data:

$$G_{w\,av} = 1500 \text{ kg}; \ B = 0.02 \text{ sec}; \ v = 500 \text{ cm/sec};$$

$$(p_w + k_t) = 1.5 \text{ kg/cm}^2; \ v = 2 \text{ and } b_t = 25 \text{ cm}.$$

The function $q_{d2} = q_{d2}\,(W_1)$ has a minimum. The value of $W_1$, corresponding to the minimum value of $q_{d2}$, varies with the parameter $n''$, which characterizes the compaction of soil during the first pass. For soils which cannot be compacted, a minimum value for $q_{d2}$ is obtained when the load is uniformly distributed over the axles ($W_1 = 1$). As the soil compaction increases, the minimum $q_{d2}$ is seen to occur at the decreasing values of $W_1$.

The magnitude of $q_{d2}$ is governed by the depth of the ruts. Hence on compacted soils, the depth of the ruts may be somewhat reduced if the front

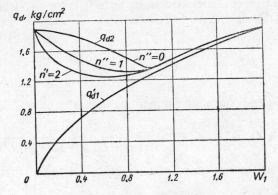

Fig. 85. The effect of load distribution on the axles of a $4 \times 4$ vehicle when a conditional specific load is put on the soil.

wheels are slightly deflated. However, this is valid only for the first pass of the machine. During subsequent passes of the vehicle over the same track, the decisive factor governing the depth of the ruts is the maximum load on the wheel. Overloading of the rear wheels inevitably leads to deeper ruts. The maximum number of passes of identical machines over the same track apparently, is possible with a uniform distribution load on the axles.

The value of $n''$ may be approximated by making use of the expression for the relative shear deformation $[q_s/(q_s-q)]$. For $q=q_s$, the soil deforms only by shear, and it does not undergo any kind of compaction. In this case, $n''=0$. When $q_s=\infty$, there is no shear deformation, and only soil deformation due to compaction is observed. In this case, $n''=1$. Values of $n''$ greater than unity are not very likely. Thus, one may assume that

$$n'' = 1 - \frac{q}{q_s}.$$

*Three axled vehicle.* 1. The load on the axles increases linearly from the front to the back $(W_1 < 1)$, $G_{w1} = W_1 G_{w\,av}$; $G_{w2} = W_2 G_{w\,av}$; $G_{w3} = (2 - W_1) G_{w\,av}$. Based on the same argument as in the previous case, we have

$$q_{d3} = \frac{K_L (q_3 - q_2)}{1 + \dfrac{Bv}{L_{w3}}} + q_{d2} \frac{1 + \dfrac{Bv}{2L_{w2}}}{1 + \dfrac{Bv}{3L_{w2}}}.$$

Replacing $K_L$, $L_w$, $q_3$ and $q_2$ and rearranging, we have

$$q_{d3} = \frac{3}{2} q'_2 \left( \frac{2A_2 \sqrt{G_{w\,av}} + Bv}{3A_2 \sqrt{G_{w\,av}} + Bv} \right) + A_1 A_2 G_{w\,av} \left[ 1 - \left( \frac{1}{2 - W_1} \right)^{\frac{1}{n''}} \right]$$

$$\times \frac{2 - W_1 - \sqrt{2 - W_1}}{A_2 \sqrt{(2 - W_1) G_{w\,av}} + Bv}. \tag{169}$$

142

2. The load on the axles decreases linearly from the front to the rear $(W_1 > 1)$. For this case,

$$q_{d3} = q_{d2} + \left( \frac{1}{1 + \dfrac{Bv}{3L_{w2}}} - \frac{1}{1 + \dfrac{Bv}{2L_{w2}}} \right) q_3.$$

Substituting and rearranging as before, we have

$$q_{d3} = q_{d2} + A_1\,A_2\,G_{w\,av}\,\sqrt{(2-W_1)}\left[ \frac{3}{3A_2\,\sqrt{G_{w\,av}}+Bv} - \frac{2}{2A_2\,\sqrt{G_{w\,av}}+Bv} \right].$$

(170)

*Four axled vehicle.* 1. If the load on the axles increases linearly from the front to the rear $(W_1 < 1)$, then

$$G_{w1} = W_1\,G_{w\,av}; \quad G_{w2} = \frac{2+W_1}{3}\,G_{w\,av} = W_2\,G_{w\,av};$$

$$G_{w3} = \frac{4-W_1}{3}\,G_{w\,av} = W_3\,G_{w\,av};$$

$$G_{w4} = (2-W_1)\,G_{w\,av} = W_4\,G_{w\,av};$$

$$q_{d4} = q_{d3}\,\frac{1+\dfrac{Bv}{4L_{w3}}}{1+\dfrac{Bv}{3L_{w3}}} + K_L\,\frac{q_4-q_3}{1+\dfrac{Bv}{L_{w4}}};$$

or

$$q_{d4} = \frac{4}{3}\,q_{d3}\left( \frac{3A_2\,\sqrt{W_3\,G_{w\,av}}+Bv}{4A_2\,\sqrt{W_3\,G_{w\,av}}+Bv} \right)$$

$$+ A_1A_2G_{w\,av}\left[ 1 - \left( \frac{W_3}{W_4} \right)^{\frac{1}{n''}} \right]\frac{W_4-\sqrt{W_4-W_3}}{A_2\,\sqrt{W_4\,G_{w\,av}}+Bv}.$$

(171)

2. If the load on the axles decreases linearly from the front to the rear $(W_1 > 1)$, then

$$q_{d4} = q_{d3} + q_4\left( \frac{1}{1+\dfrac{Bv}{4\,L_{w3}}} - \frac{1}{1+\dfrac{Bv}{3\,L_{w3}}} \right);$$

or

$$q_{d4} = q_{d3} + A_1\,A_2\,G_{w\,av}\,\sqrt{W_4}\left[ \frac{4}{4A_2\,\sqrt{W_3\,G_{w\,av}}+Bv} \right.$$

$$\left. - \frac{3}{3A_2\,\sqrt{W_3\,G_{w\,av}}+Bv} \right].$$

(172)

A study of the graph of function $q_d$ with $W_1$ for three axled and four axled vehicles for the linear load variation on the axles shows that when the number of axles is large, the front wheels have a greater compaction action on the soil. The optimal value of $q_d$ moves towards the decreasing values of $W_1$.

For noncohesive soils, the minimum value of $q_d$, irrespective of the number of axles, is obtained when the load is distributed uniformly over the axles.

The effect of the nonuniform load distribution, on the depth of the ruts formed by the wheels, is governed by the functions $h = h(q)$ and $q_d = q_d(W_1)$.

Figure 86 shows the relationship between the depth of the ruts formed by the wheels as a function of the load distribution on the axles of a three axled vehicle. This graph (Fig. 86) shows the increase in the depth of the ruts $h_1$, $h_2$ and $h_3$ after passage of the wheels on the first, second and third axles for different values of $W_1$ (the nature of load distribution, in all cases, is linear).

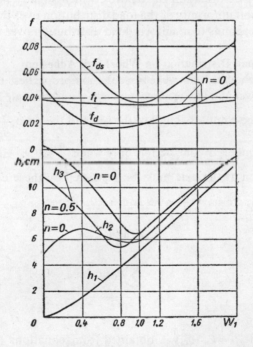

Fig. 86. Effect of the load distribution on the axles of a three axled vehicle and on the depth of the ruts and rolling resistance for $n=0$ (results obtained on an electronic computer: tire type: 12.00-18; $G_{w\ av}=1500$ kg; soil parameters: $\phi_0=16°$; $c_0=0.08$ kg/cm$^2$; $E=15$ kg/cm$^2$; $H_s=30$ cm; $\gamma=1.1$ g/cm$^3$; $a=1$; $\phi_r=0.3$; $E'=2$ kg/cm$^2$).

The smallest depth of wheel rut for noncohesive soils is obtained when the load distribution on the axles is uniform; while for cohesive soils, this occurs when the front axle is slightly off-loaded ($W_1\approx0.7$-0.9).

### Effect of Axle Load Distribution on Rolling Resistance

The principal component of rolling resistance, which is caused by the energy expended on the compaction of soil $f_c$, is governed by the total depth of ruts formed by the wheels. Hence, the nature of this relationship is governed by the functional relationship $h = h(W_1)$ (Fig. 86).

The second component of rolling resistance is the resistance to the bulldozer effect $f_b$, which depends upon the depth of the ruts formed by the wheels on each axle. Since resistance to bulldozing increases progressively with the increasing depth of the ruts, its minimum value should be expected for uniform increase in the depth of the ruts caused by the passage of wheels on each axle. It may be observed from Fig. 86 that this occurs when $W_1 < 1$ (for the case considered $n'' = 0$ and $W_1 \approx 0.7$).

The third component of rolling resistance $f_t$ is governed by the energy expended on the deformation of the tires, which slightly increases with the increase in the nonuniformity of the load distribution over the axles. Its minimum value corresponds to a uniform load distribution over the axles.

### Effect of Axle Load Distribution on Wheel-Soil Adhesion

On soils which have homogeneous cohesion properties, the nature of the relationship between the adhesion coefficient $\phi$ and the axle load distribution is governed by the compressibility of the soil and the ratio $\dfrac{q}{q_s}$. One may expect the soil to undergo compaction only when $\dfrac{q}{q_s} < 0.9$. Hence, the maximum load applied at the axle must be restricted by these conditions. If for any value of $W_1$, we have $\dfrac{q}{q_s} < 0.9$ and $B > 0$, then

$$\tau_{\max i} = q'_{di} \tan \phi_0 + c_0;$$

$$\phi_{av} = \frac{\sum\limits_{1}^{N} P_a(q_{di})}{G_a}. \tag{173}$$

The function $P_a = P_a(q_{di})$ is obtained from equations (117), (169) and (170). The values of $G_{wi}$ and its corresponding values of $q'_{d1}$, $q'_{d2}$ and $q'_{d3}$ are tabulated (see p. 145) to obtain the example under consideration ($N = 3$; $G_{w\ av} = 1500$ kg; $A_1 = 0.0393$, $A_2 = 1.29$, $Bv = 10$ cm).

The average value of the wheel-soil adhesion coefficient $\phi_{av}$ is determined from these data. As can be seen from Fig. 87, for soils which are homogeneous in the depthwise direction, the load distribution on the axles has practically no influence on the total wheel-soil adhesion force.

If the top layer of the soil has very high adhesive properties compared to

| Parameter | Coefficient of load distribution for the front axle, $W_1$ | | | | | | |
|---|---|---|---|---|---|---|---|
| | 0 | 0.4 | 0.8 | 1 | 1.2 | 1.6 | 2.0 |
| $G_{w1}$ | 0 | 344 | 800 | 1030 | 1270 | 1750 | 2280 |
| $G_{w2}$ | 1010 | 1380 | 1200 | 1230 | 1265 | 1290 | 1330 |
| $G_{w3}$ | 2530 | 2110 | 1440 | 1330 | 1060 | 547 | 0 |
| $q_1'$ | 0 | 0.73 | 1.11 | 1.26 | 1.4 | 1.66 | 1.88 |
| $q_2'$ | 1.25 | 1.45 | 1.36 | 1.38 | 1.39 | 1.41 | 1.43 |
| $q_3'$ | 1.99 | 1.8 | 1.49 | 1.43 | 1.28 | 0.92 | 0 |

the underlying one, then the total wheel-soil adhesion force is a maximum when the load is distributed uniformly over the axles. In a case when the axle load distribution is not uniform, the sinkage of the overloaded wheel into the soil increases, and the wheels come in contact with a far weaker layer of the soil.

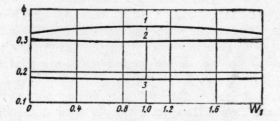
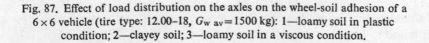

Fig. 87. Effect of load distribution on the axles on the wheel-soil adhesion of a $6 \times 6$ vehicle (tire type: 12.00–18, $G_{w\ av} = 1500$ kg): 1—loamy soil in plastic condition; 2—clayey soil; 3—loamy soil in a viscous condition.

On nonhomogeneous soils whose cohesive properties increase with depth, adhesion is greater with the deeper sinkage of the wheel into the soil. Hence, for increasing nonuniformity in the load distribution on the axles, there is an increase in the total force of adhesion.

In conclusion, it may be observed that a minimum depth for the ruts formed by the wheels and a minimum rolling resistance are obtained when the load on the axles is characterized by $W_1 = 0.8$–1.

The maximum wheel-soil adhesion for the vehicle, for various values of $W_1$, depends upon the nature of the variation of the soil's cohesive properties along its depth.

## EFFECT OF KINEMATIC WHEEL IMBALANCE ON THE PERFORMANCE OF A MULTIAXLED VEHICLE

In recent years, attempts have been made to improve the tractive properties of wheeled tractors and automobiles by introducing kinematic imbalance* between the wheels mounted on different axles. Experimental results have established that, in certain cases, introduction of a kinematic imbalance helps in reducing the power required to drive the vehicle by 5 to 10%. For dry sandy soils, the optimal value of such an unbalance was found to be nearly 10%.

On the basis of certain theoretical assumptions, it can be considered in principle whether it is possible to reduce the power expended on driving a vehicle by the kinematic imbalance of its wheels.

Comparing the wheel-soil interaction parameters of the front and rear wheels of an automobile, it has been observed that, in most cases, the front wheel interacts with a weak soil; while all the wheels that follow this route run over a compacted soil. The first wheel forms a deep rut and hence, the length and angle of contact of the front wheels with the soil is greater than those of the succeeding wheels. With all other conditions remaining the same, the front wheel tire undergoes a small deformation.

The depth of the ruts and the rolling resistance depend upon the direction of the elementary forces at the wheel-soil contact zone. The greater the angle $\beta$ (see Fig. 33), the greater the forward displacement of the soil and, as a result, both the depth of the ruts and the rolling resistance increase. Angle $\beta$ depends upon the wheel slip.

A rut is mainly formed by the leading curvilinear portion of the contact zone. When $\beta_i \approx 0$, one would expect the depth of rut and rolling resistance to be a minimum in this zone. Since angle $\beta_i$ is different at different points in the zone, an optimal summation $\Sigma \beta_i$ for the given zone may be conceived. In the very first approximation, the optimal value of the coefficient of slippage is found to be

$$\delta_{s\ opt} = 1 - \frac{R - \delta - (0.3-0.5)\,h}{R_{w0}}. \qquad (174)$$

Thus, it is desirable to have greater wheel slippage with an increase in the depth of the ruts. In conformity with the relationship between the values of $h$ for the front and following wheels, the kinematic imbalance must be such that the rotational speed of the front wheel is greater than that of the following wheels. When the load on the axles is uniformly distributed and the

*Kinematic imbalance is the concept of allowing different rotational speeds for the wheels mounted on different axles of the automobile, which is achieved by providing unequal gear ratios or unequal rolling radii.

inflation pressure is identical, a slight imbalance in the desired direction is seen to occur due to the difference in the radial deformation of the tires on the front and succeeding wheels. In such a case, with an increase in the depth of the ruts formed by the front wheels, the difference in the deformations increases and the imbalance, correspondingly, also increases. The kinematic imbalance of the wheels can be controlled to some extent by regulating the inflation pressure. Figure 88 shows a graph for the variation of the rolling radius as a function of the depth of the ruts for various inflation pressures. When $p_w$=const., the imbalance due to the effect of the depth of the rut on tire deformation may lie between 0.5 and 2%. The inflation pressure has a far more significant effect on the rolling radius. The kinematic imbalance can be brought up to 7% by varying the inflation pressure $p_w$ in the tires. However, this method is not very practicable since increasing the pressure $p_w$ in the front tires leads to a considerable increase in the depth of the ruts.

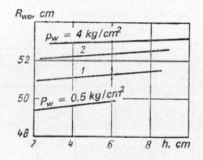

Fig. 88. Variation of the rolling radius as a function of the depth of the ruts $h$ and the inflation pressure in the tires (tire type: 12.00–18; $G_w$=1500 kg).

Some modern, highly mobile automobiles are equipped with an overrunning (free-wheeling) clutch to automatically couple the front axle when driving conditions become difficult. This seems to cause greater skidding of the rear wheels due to kinematic imbalance. This imbalance leads to higher power losses due to the rolling of the wheels. When the rear axle is decoupled, the use of an overrunning clutch is very well-justified. In such a case, only the front wheels act as the driving wheels when the vehicle is running on roads with a hard top dressing. In both the cases, use of an overrunning clutch increases the danger of the soil tearing off at the contact surface.

In the above discussion, the problem of wheel-soil adhesion and slippage, which sometimes has a decisive influence not only on the mobility of the vehicle (off-the-road mobility) but also on the power required for its locomotion, has not been touched upon.

The characteristic factors $P_a=P_{a1}+P_{a2}=P_a$ ($\delta_s$) for different values of kinematic imbalance are shown in Fig. 89 (suffixes 1 and 2 refer to the first and the second axles). The relationship between kinematic imbalance and the slippage coefficient may be expressed by the following equation:

$$\delta_s = 1 - \frac{v_a}{\omega_{av}\, R_{w0}}; \quad \delta_{s1} = 1 - \frac{v_a}{\omega_1\, R_{w0}};$$

$$\delta_{s2} = 1 - \frac{v_a}{\omega_2\, R_{w0}}; \quad \rho_w = 1 - \frac{\omega_2}{\omega_1};$$

$$\delta_{s1} = 1 - (1 - \delta_s)\frac{2 - \rho_w}{2};$$

$$\delta_{s2} = 1 - (1 - \delta_s)\frac{(2 - \rho_w)}{2(1 - \rho_w)}, \tag{175}$$

where $\omega_1$ and $\omega_2$ are the angular velocities of the wheels mounted on the first and second axles;

$\omega_{av}$ is the average angular velocity;

$\rho_w$ is the kinematic imbalance.

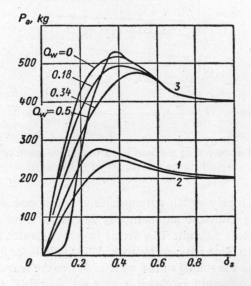

Fig. 89. Relationship between the wheel-soil adhesive force $P_a$ of a 4 × 4 vehicle and slippage and the kinematic imbalance of the wheels: 1—for the front wheels; 2—for the rear wheels; 3—$P_{a1} + P_{a2}$ (tire type: 12.00–18; $G_w = 1500$ kg; for soil parameters—see Fig. 86).

A vehicle's wheel-soil adhesion characteristics are found to improve when there is no kinematic imbalance. In case of an unbalance in either direction, the total adhesion force decreases over the entire range of variation of the slippage coefficient ($\delta_s < 0.3$–0.4). The decrease in the adhesion force $P_a$ is negligible in the range of the values of the kinematic imbalance conventionally used ($\rho_w \leqslant 0.2$). The adhesion force $P_a = P_a$ ($\delta_s$) rapidly deteriorates at large negative values of the kinematic imbalance.

From the above discussion, the basic conclusion that follows is that for present-day application as well as future investigations, the introduction of a positive kinematic imbalance of up to 20% does not actually impair the wheel-soil adhesion characteristics of the vehicle.

The desirability of introducing an imbalance must be judged on the basis of the power requirement of the vehicle. When $\delta_s \leqslant 0.3$, the introduction of a positive imbalance up to 10% may reduce the power demand of the vehicle by 3–4%. For an imbalance up to 20%, the power requirement can be reduced by 6%. When $\delta_s > 0.3$, the introduction of an imbalance does not in any way reduce the power requirement for locomotion.

The effect of introducing a kinematic imbalance depends upon the soil properties. It increases with an increase of the friction angle $\phi_0$ of the soil and an increase of the load bearing capacity of the soil $q_s$ and its modulus of deformation $E$.

## SPECIAL FEATURES OF WHEEL–SOIL INTERACTION OF A MULTIWHEELED VEHICLE

The maximum possible values of the performance parameters of a multi-wheeled vehicle may be obtained by a summation of the performance parameters of individual wheels running over a single track. The actual values of the performance parameters of multiwheeled vehicles may differ considerably from the maximum possible. The inevitable deviations are due to the following reasons:

i) diversity in the mechanical properties of the soil under the different wheels of the vehicle;

ii) redistribution of the vertical load depending upon the conditions and mode of locomotion;

iii) vibrations of the automobile body;

iv) the changing kinematic imbalance of the wheels caused by changes in the vertical load;

v) effect of the parameters of power drive on the wheels.

### Effect of Soil Surface Heterogeneity

The mechanical properties of most natural soil surfaces are remarkably heterogeneous. The structural properties of soils may differ several times over a distance equal to the base of a multiwheeled vehicle.

The performance characteristics of wheels vary in conformity with the variations of the soil parameters. In the case of multi-axled vehicles, the range of variation of performance parameters is far smaller than for a single wheel; since at every instant of time, different wheels are in contact with the soil tracts of different properties. The greater the length of the wheel base of the vehicle and the larger the number of wheels, the greater is the averaging action. Tractor-trailers with a direct drive have the greatest averaging action. Hence, on soils which are highly heterogeneous, the advantageous properties of self-powered tractor-trailers are more and more pronounced.

Let us determine the possible averaging of parameters on dirt path. If there is no restriction on the power of the vehicle and, at every point on the path, the wheel-soil adhesion is fully utilized, then the maximum speed expressed as a function of the coordinates of the path may be expressed by the equation

$$v_{\max} = \sqrt{2g \int_0^s \phi_T \, ds};$$

i.e., the speed of the vehicle, governed by the limiting wheel-soil adhesion, is determined by the total area enclosed by the curve $\phi_T = \phi_T(s)$ and the abscissa. If this area turns out to be negative, then all motion ceases. Consequently, even when the power available to the vehicle is unlimited, the parameters should not be averaged over the entire path.

In fact, in most cases the total draw bar pull by adhesion may not be entirely realised due to the limited power available to the vehicle as well as to the restriction placed on the vehicle speed from considerations of safety and smooth riding conditions. Hence, it becomes necessary to isolate the regions which have a negative traction coefficient as well as those with a very large value of $\phi_T$, which could never be realised. The problem which then emerges is "what is the extent to which one can tolerate the roughness of a given route?" As a first approximation, one may recommend a scale which would enable the isolation of tracts of length equal to that of the wheel base of the vehicle on the route map.

### Vertical Load Variation on Wheels during Locomotion

The variation of vertical load on the wheels during locomotion is primarily due to three reasons. These are the gradient of the path, reaction moments and the forces acting on the body of the automobile and vibrations of the body.

The normal soil reaction at every axle can be expressed as a function of forces and moments with the help of the diagram represented in Fig. 90 [57]. Assuming the rigidity of the suspension of all wheels to be identical ($c_{pi} = $ const.), we have

$$G_a \cos \alpha' = 2 \sum_{i=1}^N G_{wi}; \quad G_a \sin \alpha' + \frac{G_a}{g} j = \sum_{i=1}^N T_i;$$

$$l_0 G_a \cos \alpha' + \sum_{i=1}^{N} M_{fi} + \sum_{i=1}^{N} T_i h_d = 2 \sum_{i=1}^{N} G_{wi} l_i.$$

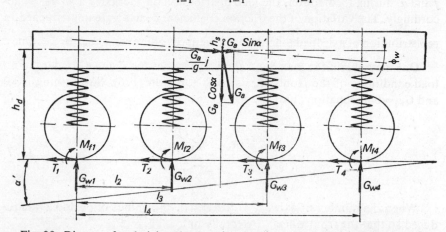

Fig. 90. Diagram for deriving the equation for the vertical loads on wheels of a multiwheeled vehicle.

Apart from this, the normal reaction may also be expressed in terms of the rigidity of the suspension $c_p$ and the parameters of displacement of the chassis $(h_0, \phi_w)$

$$2 G_{wi} = c_p [h_0 - (l_0 - l_i) \tan \phi_w];$$

$$2 \sum_{i=1}^{N} G_{wi} = c_p \left[ N h_0 - \left( N l_0 - \sum_{i=1}^{N} l_i \right) \tan \phi_w \right].$$

Solving the above equations and considering that

$$\sum_{i=1}^{N} M_{fi} = G_a f R_{w0}; \quad \sum_{i=1}^{N} T_i = G_a \phi_T;$$

we have

$$G_{wi} = \frac{G_a}{2N} \left\{ \cos \alpha' + \left[ N (\phi_T h_d + f R_{w0}) \right. \right.$$

$$\left. \left. + \left( N l_0 - \sum_{i=1}^{N} l_i \right) \right] \cos \alpha' \frac{N l_i - \sum_{i=1}^{N} l_i}{N \sum_{i=1}^{N} l_i^2 - \left( \sum_{i=1}^{N} l_i \right)^2} \right\} . \quad (176)$$

It follows from equation (176) that redistribution of the load over the axles occurs at all operating conditions. Because of the continuous variation of $\phi_T$, $f$ and $\alpha'$ during locomotion, the load distribution on the axles also varies accordingly. The variation of the traction coefficient $\phi_T$ has a greater influence on redistribution of axle load than the coefficient of rolling resistance by $\dfrac{h_d}{R_{w0}}$ times.

One may obtain the maximum allowable values for $\alpha'$ and $\phi_T$ under the no load conditions of the front wheels from equation (176). Substituting $l_1 = 0$ and $G_{w1} = 0$ in equation (176), we have

$$\frac{\phi_T h_d + f R_{w0}}{\cos \alpha'} = \frac{\sum\limits_{i=1}^{N} l_i^2}{\sum\limits_{i=1}^{N} l_i} - l_0. \tag{177}$$

When the number of axles $N$ is increased, the values of $\phi_T$ and $\alpha'$ are reduced so that the front wheels are totally unloaded.

### Specific Features of Locomotion on a Gradient

The following additional difficulties are encountered when an automobile moves over a gradient:

i) the tractive force required for locomotion increases and, simultaneously, the sum of the normal reactions of the soil ($G_a \cos \alpha'$) reduces;

ii) the front wheels deflate and, as a result, the losses incurred on controlling the vehicle increase;

iii) the rear wheels deflate so that the direction of the load acting on them moves farther away from the normal to the soil surface.

Because of these, the motion of a vehicle on a gradient is restricted by several factors.

1. Insufficient traction of the vehicle

$$\frac{M_v \, i_{tr} \, \eta_{tr}}{R_{w0}} < G_a^{\bullet} \left( f \cos \alpha + \sin \alpha + \frac{j}{g} \right), \tag{178}$$

where $j$ is the acceleration of the automobile;

$M_v$ is the momentum of the vehicle;

$i_{tr}$ is the transmission gear ratio;

$\eta_{tr}$ is the transmission efficiency.

2. Insufficient wheel-soil adhesion,

$$\phi < \left( f_s \cos \alpha + \sin \alpha + \frac{j}{g} \right). \tag{179}$$

3. Longitudinal overturning of the automobile,

$$\tan \alpha > \frac{L_a - a}{h_d}.$$

4. Front wheels lifting off the ground [equation (176)].

5. Inadequate load bearing capacity of the soil under the rear wheels in the absence of an underlying firm soil layer.

As may be observed from equation (105), when the value of $q$ approaches $q_s$, $h$ tends to infinity. The magnitude of $q_s$ is determined from equation (78); while that of $q$ from equations (111) and (176).

## Special Features of Locomotion on a Hillside

When a vehicle moves on a hillside, the load on the axles gets redistributed in the transverse direction:

$$G_{w\ max} = \left( \frac{\cos \beta_a}{2} + \frac{h_d}{B} \sin \beta_a \right) G_0; \qquad (180)$$

$$G_{w\ min} = \left( \frac{\cos \beta_a}{2} - \frac{h_d}{\beta} \sin \beta_a \right) G_0, \qquad (181)$$

where $\beta_a$ is the angle of the sidewise tilting of the automobile;

$G_0$ is the load acting on the axles.

The motion of a vehicle on a hillside slope may be constrained by the wheel-soil adhesion, its tendency to overturn and the poor load bearing capacity of the soil.

The constraint due to wheel-soil adhesion may be expressed by the inequality

$$\sqrt{(G_w \sin \beta_a)^2 + [G_w (\phi_T + f_s)]^2} < G_w \phi \cos \beta_a.$$

The left hand side of the inequality is the total force applied at the axles of the wheels; while the right hand side represents the wheel-soil adhesion force.

Rearranging the expression, we have

$$\beta_a < \cos^{-1} \sqrt{\frac{1 + (\phi_T + f_s)^2}{1 + \phi^2}}. \qquad (182)$$

If locomotion is to be ensured on a hillside where $\beta_a = 25°$, $\phi_T = 0.2$ and $f = 0.1$, the adhesion coefficient $\phi$ must be greater than 0.58.

The constraint due to the tendency to overturn is expressed by the inequality

$$\beta_a < \tan^{-1} \frac{B_a}{2h_d},$$

where $B_a$ is the width of the track;

$h_d$ is the height at which the center of gravity of the vehicle is located.

The constraint due to the load bearing capacity of the soil (soils which do not have an underlying firm base) may be expressed by the inequality $q_{max} < q_s$.

Expressing $q_s$ from equations (73) and (78) and $q_{max}$ from equation

$$q = \frac{(p_w + k_t)\, \delta U}{b_t H}$$

and equations (117) and (118), we have

$$G_0 < A \frac{X_1\, b_t\, \dfrac{\pi - 4 \tan \phi_0\, \beta_a}{\pi + 4 \tan \phi_0\, \beta_a} + X_2 \dfrac{3\pi - 2\beta_a}{3\pi + 2\beta_a}}{\dfrac{\cos \beta_a}{2} + \dfrac{h_d}{B} \sin \beta_a}, \tag{183}$$

where $A$ is a parameter which is a constant for a given set of soil and tires,

$$A = \left( \zeta_z \frac{a b_t}{E} \right)^2 \left\{ \frac{EH}{\zeta_z a U (p_w + k_t)} - 1 + \sqrt{\left[ \frac{(p_w + k_t)\, U \zeta_z\, a}{EH} \right]^2 - 1 - \frac{2\, EH}{\zeta_z a U\, (p_w + k_t)}} \right\}.$$

If it is assumed that $\dfrac{h_d}{B_a} = 0.75$ and $X_1 = 0$, then the permissible axle load based on the soil bearing capacity on a hillside (with a positive gradient of $25°$) decreases by almost twice in comparison to that of level ground.

### Special Characteristics of Wheel–Soil Interaction of Multiwheeled Vehicles Moving over a Curved Path

In contrast to linear locomotion, when a vehicle moves over a curved path
1) a lateral force acts on the wheels;
2) the wheels in one of the tracks do not move;
3) the load on the axles is redistributed due to the action of the centrifugal force;
4) each of the wheels forms a very wide rut.

Consider the case of a two axled automobile during cornering at a constant radius (Fig. 91). For motion without drift, the width of the rut is given by

$$b_w = \sqrt{\left( R_1 + \frac{b}{2} \right)^2 + \left( \frac{l}{2} \right)^2} - \left( R_1 - \frac{b}{2} \right), \tag{184}$$

where $R_1$ is the distance between the center of rotation and the center of the contact zone.

In case of drift

$$b_w = b \cos \alpha + l \sin \alpha. \tag{185}$$

The width of the ruts increases with an increase of the drift angle.

If the front wheels are not the driving wheels, then the tractive force exerted by the rear wheels pushes the front wheels at some angle to their plane of rotation. Due to this, a lateral force appears and the tractive force required to sustain motion increases. The optimal case during cornering is one in which all the wheels freewheel without transmitting either tractive or braking forces to the automobile body. The lateral force gives rise to an additional deformation of the soil together with additional rolling losses. The lateral force and the total rolling losses increase with an increase of the cornering angle of the wheels.

When the wheels get locked during cornering, they get into an unfavorable misalignment. This misalignment is governed by the relationship between the radii of the wheels and the turning radius of the automobile and its framework.

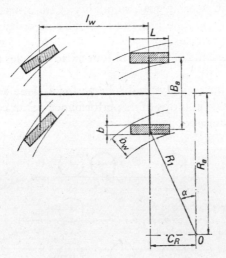

Fig. 91. Cornering of a two axled automobile.

The criteria for evaluating the maneuverability of transport vehicles (automobiles) were formulated by Ya.E. Farobin [66]. He arbitrarily subdivided it into two types: static and dynamic. Static maneuverability is characterized by the ability of the automobile to execute a smooth turn with a small radius of turning and at modest speeds. The ability of an automobile to execute a non-uniform turn at high speeds was designated as dynamic maneuverability.

Maneuverability should be static for motion on soft soils. The parameters which are employed to estimate the static maneuverability of vehicles include the minimum turning radius, the specific resistance to motion during turning and the wheel-soil adhesion force during turning. The coefficient of utilization of the wheel-soil adhesion force during turning equals the ratio of the total tractive effort developed by the vehicle to the potentially possible adhesion force. The smaller this ratio, the lesser the probability of loss of maneuverability due to loss of mobility.

When the coordinates $C_R$ and $R_a$ for the center of the turning of a machine are known, then the static maneuverability parameters may be determined with the help of equations (105) to (116) and (185).

## COMPARATIVE EVALUATION OF THE ARRANGEMENT OF MULTIAXLED VEHICLES

The arrangement of multiaxled vehicles determines its ability to cross ditches and surmount obstacles, the redistribution of the load over the wheels (axles) during locomotion, the stability of motion, the suitability of suspensions, the resistance to cornering over soft soils, the maneuverability of the automobile, the complexity of the steering gear, suitability of transmission arrangements, the layout of the automobile and the feasibility of utilizing mass-produced components of road vehicles.

Possible arrangements of three and four axled vehicles are shown in Figs. 92 and 93.

At present, the most widely used scheme for a three axled vehicle is the 1–2 arrangement, since in terms of its performance parameters, it is the most suitable for use on automobile roads.

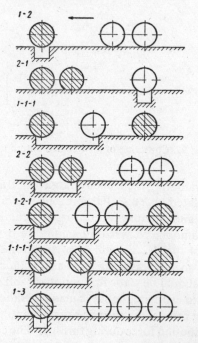

Fig. 92. Wheel arrangements of multiaxled vehicles (the shaded portions show the optimal disposition of steering controlled wheels).

When such an arrangement is used, the automobile becomes simple in design as well as inexpensive in cost. One axle is sufficient for steering purposes. A simple balanced suspension may be used for the two rear axles. For transmission purposes, it does not actually require the installation of another differential between the two rear axles. Compared to other wheel arrangements, these vehicles may extensively utilize interchangeable mass-produced components of road vehicles.

For locomotion on uneven roads or paths, this type of arrangement is not optimal since, firstly, it would not be capable of surmounting the horizontal obstacles (ditches), which are more than two-thirds of the wheel diameter. Secondly, the curvature of the longitudinal profile of the path becomes larger than for other arrangements, and as a result, there is a greater danger of the automobile body grazing the road while it turns over road convexities (ridges).

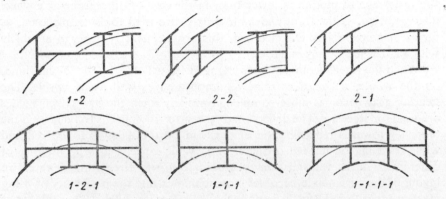

Fig. 93. Cornering (turning) of a multiaxled vehicle.

The characteristic features of 1–2 arrangements on soft soil surfaces are: considerable loss of maneuverability and higher resistance to cornering because of the extremely wider ruts formed by the two sets of rear wheels. In the case of trucks running empty, the load on the front wheels becomes considerably greater than that on the rear wheels, which on most soils results in poor traction quality for the automobile.

The 2–1 wheel arrangement is seldom used and then only on those machines where the center of gravity is displaced towards the front. In this arrangement, the two front axles are used for steering and, hence, the construction of the automobile becomes more complicated. However, the maneuverability of the machine improves.

During the execution of a turn, the wheels develop six different ruts. The total rolling resistance on soft soils may be greater than that for vehicles with the previous wheel arrangement; while on hard surfaces, it may be lower.

The 1–1–1 wheel arrangement is most suitable for automobiles designed for use on an uneven and easily deformable soil surface. When the center of gravity is located above the middle axle, the deflection of the suspension is restricted and when special techniques are adopted for driving the vehicle, it is possible to surmount ditches which are as wide as the distance between the axles.

While passing over ridges, there is practically no danger of the automobile body scraping the soil surface. At the same time, it should be noted that for motion over an undulating "wavy" surface, the wheels on one of the axles could completely lift off the ground or a severe redistribution of the load on the axles could occur—far more frequently than in the case of the 1–2 wheel arrangement.

In a case where the two extreme axles are used for steering the vehicle, performance during turning appears to be better. While turning on soft soils, the resistance to motion is lower than in the case of other three-axle wheel arrangements. If the front and middle axles are used for steering, then, as far as maneuverability is concerned, this arrangement is closer to a vehicle with a 2–1 wheel arrangement.

When the wheel arrangement is changed from 1–2 to 1–1–1, the machine, on the whole, becomes extremely complicated as well as expensive. The steering gear becomes more complex, especially when the two extreme axles are used for steering. The deflection of the suspension needs to be large if the tendency towards redistribution of the load on the axles is to be reduced while traveling on uneven surfaces. The vehicle needs a large number of differentials in its transmission to eliminate power circulation. The entire layout of the automobile becomes more complex and the possibility of using mass-produced road vehicle components becomes less likely. The stability of the automobile worsens while traveling on slippery roads. This arrangement becomes unsuitable for a towing vehicle.

Use of a four axled vehicle helps in reducing axle loading and the size of the tires. It improves the geometric parameters for trafficability and the off-the-road mobility of the automobile on most soft soils. The range of road-soil conditions over which the vehicle can be used becomes greater. At the same time, the construction of the automobile becomes more complex and its maintenance and servicing take longer.

The 2–2 wheel arrangement allows a much simpler construction of the four axled automobile. Since the axles are in adjacent pairs, the suspension most frequently used is a balanced one. Good maneuverability occurs if the two front axles are used for steering. In this case, the steering gear is simpler than in the case when the extreme axles are used for steering.

Since it is not possible to locate a differential between the closely spaced axle pair, one may use a simple transmission, which includes a distribution box with two output shafts and driving gears for the middle axles with the universal joint shafts passing through them.

Vehicles with a 2–2 arrangement ensure a better stability during linear locomotion on roads as well as the least load redistribution on the axles, while running over a rough terrain.

The disadvantages of a 2–2 wheel arrangement vehicle include: i) a comparatively small width for the ditches that can be passed (this is governed by the distance between adjacent wheels); ii) a large radius for the longitudinal road profile (because of the large distance between the two middle axles); iii) high rolling resistance during cornering on soft soils (because of the formation of six different wheel ruts of which two are wider); and iv) a certain increase in soil deformation caused by the closely spaced axle pairs.

The 1–2–1 wheel arrangement provides extremely favorable geometric parameters for off-the-road mobility, especially in the bridging of wide ditches. Apart from this, the automobile has better maneuverability when the two extreme axles are used for steering the vehicle.

The rolling resistance during turning or cornering on soft soils is found to be lower than that for a 2–2 arrangement, since only four wheel ruts are formed.

While moving over a rough wavy terrain, the redistribution of the axle load is greater than in the previous case. The extreme wheels or those in the center could lose contact with the soil, leading to higher loads on the transmission, suspension, tires and chassis. The traction efficiency of the automobile also decreases. When the wheels on the extreme axles lift off the ground, the automobile may be difficult to control. In order to eliminate all the above defects, it becomes necessary to increase the span of the suspension.

When a 1–2–1 wheel arrangement is adopted, the construction of the automobile becomes more complicated, resulting in a complex steering gear, suspension and transmission.

The 1–1–1–1 wheel arrangement of a vehicle is an intermediate scheme. For such an arrangement, the steering axles are either the first two or the front and rear ones. But in both cases, the maneuverability of the automobile is poorer than the first two arrangements. One of the advantages of a vehicle with an identical distance between the axles is its arrangement of the longitudinal spacing of the vehicle's torsion bars, irrespective of the type of suspension, and an extremely favorable load transfer to the soil.

Vehicles with a 1–3 or 3–1 wheel arrangement are used when the automobile's center of gravity is unfavorably located. These arrangements, however, do not ensure that the vehicle would be capable of crossing wide ditches nor do they provide good maneuverability for the automobile.

Vehicles equipped with large diameter front wheels are of considerable interest. Increasing the diameter of the front wheels reduces their bulldozer effect as well as the rolling resistance, improves soil compaction and the vehicle's ability to surmount such obstacles as sills, trenches and ditches.

For an off-the-road vehicle, a single wheel on an axle with identical ruts for all the wheels is considered to be the most advantageous. For most soil conditions, especially in the case of soils which undergo compaction and those with a thin deformable top layer, such vehicles have the lowest rolling resistance and the highest wheel-soil adhesion. The exceptions to these are weak turf covered soils and yielding soils without an underlying firm base, in which a characteristic feature is the increase in the depth of the ruts with each successive pass of a wheel. For locomotion on such soils, it is desirable that each wheel rolls in a new track.

Experience shows many cases which deviate from the generally accepted recommendations. This is explained by the conflicting influence of the extremely large number of requirements that confront an automobile designer.

## COMBINED TRACTION VEHICLES

The optimal parameters of a vehicle widely differ depending upon the properties of the various soil surfaces. For a wheeled machine to move with ease over yielding soils (turf covered, waterlogged, virgin snow fields with a soft snow cover $H_s > 1$ m, period of poor road conditions), there is such a severe increase in the dimensions required for the wheeled vehicle that the automobile becomes almost unsuitable for highway driving. Its performance becomes disproportionately small compared to a road vehicle.

A vehicle could be considered to be most versatile when all its basic parameters could be varied during the process of operation. So far in the multiwheeled vehicles under consideration, one may vary the inflation pressure in the tires and the vertical load (by varying the transported cargo) during operation.

The versatility of an automobile could be significantly improved by using combined traction vehicles, i.e. vehicles which provide several combinations of design and operating parameters.

Let us enumerate the various possible types of combined traction vehicles. These are as follows:

i) wheeled vehicles with interchangeable devices to improve off-the-road mobility;

ii) vehicles with a variable number of driving wheels;

iii) wheel and crawler track driven vehicles;

iv) wheel and step vehicles.

### Wheeled Vehicles with Detachable Devices for Improving Off-the-road Mobility

When certain attachments are used to increase wheel-soil adhesion, the range of operation of the automobile increases considerably and the traction properties of wheeled tractors also improve.

Fine-linked chains, which significantly increase the traction properties of automobiles on mud, snow and ice covered roads, are widely used on road vehicles. Chains in the form of a net (mesh) provide good road adhesion—in both longitudinal and lateral directions. Fine-linked chains in the form of a ladder provide poor adhesion in the lateral direction, but they are cheaper and far simpler to manufacture.

Poor abrasion resistance is the principal disadvantage of linked chains. To overcome this difficulty, chains have been devised in which each link on the tread-band has a roller, which protects it against wear and improves the wheel-soil adhesion. The local wear of the tire is the second disadvantage of chains. Tire wear is considerably reduced when tires are fitted with bracelet-link type chains, in which the link on the tread band is made of an elastic material. However, these are not much effective on ice covered winter roads.

While moving over yielding soils, fine-linked and bracelet-linked chains are not very effective due to the small height of the lugs. Track chains with long lugs of different shapes are used for motion on soft soils (Fig. 94). Rhombus shaped track elements have been found to be ideal. Apart from chains which go all around the tires, far simpler devices to improve the off-the-road mobility of vehicles can be used. These are: bracelets or bands made up of link or track element chains, anti-skid shoes and elastic patches. These fittings are substantially lighter and faster to mount on the wheel. If it is absolutely essential to fit chains on the wheels before approaching a difficult terrain which may take 10 to 15 minutes to traverse, then bracelets and shoes should be mounted just before the automobile gets stuck, and the time required to carry out this should not exceed 5 minutes. However, the locomotion of an automobile with bracelets or shoes mounted on its tires is less uniform. These devices are suitable for routes where difficult road conditions prevail at a few places and which stretch over short length of soft soil.

The frequent use of detachable devices for improving the off-the-road mobility of automobiles may be explained by the following: i) the large mass and volume of the metal fitting; ii) difficulty in the mounting of the wheels and their subsequent removal; iii) the need for transporting them; iv) the danger of tire damage due to the hard elements of the fittings; and v) insufficient knowledge about the economic advantages of such devices.

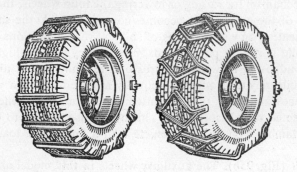

Fig. 94. Track chains.

Preliminary calculations and experiments show that the use of detachable lugs on the driving wheels of road vehicles (ZIL-130 and GAZ-53), when operating on many difficult soil surfaces (dirt roads during rainy season, etc.), improves the off-the-road mobility of these automobiles to the level of multi-drive vehicles (GAZ-66, ZIL-131). Under such conditions, the economic advantage of using the ZIL-130 and GAZ-53 automobiles instead of the GAZ-66 and ZIL-131 vehicles is beyond any doubt.

The significant advantage in using such mountings for improving off-the-road mobility is the possible selection of parameters for these fittings, for specific local conditions during different periods of the year, and the economic merit of utilizing different types of fittings during different periods of the year.

When detachable lugs are used on multi-drive automobiles, including those with variable inflation tires, the range of soil conditions over which such automobiles may be operated likewise becomes much greater.

On soft soils, elastic lugs are found to be highly effective. Under the action of soil forces, they change their position relative to the tire [64].

### Vehicles with a Variable Number of Wheels in Operation

It is well-known that there are machines in actual use for which the locomotion device consists of two to three axles, that are constantly in operation, and one or two axles, which occupy two positions—a lowered position (working mode) and a raised position (Fig. 95). When such vehicles are used, the main wheels are equipped for running on hard, paved roads. The parameters of the auxiliary wheels are selected from the view of making the vehicle more versatile and reliable.

The wheel arrangement of a vehicle with two pairs of auxiliary wheels may be accomplished in several ways.

*Variant I* (Fig. 95a). The tires on the auxiliary wheels are of the same size as the main wheels. If the auxiliary wheels are lowered, the automobile runs as a normal four axled vehicle. When this combination is used in a vehicle with a mechanism for raising or lowering the four wheels, the design and construction of the automobile becomes complicated. At the same time, its effective utilization on various types of soil and road conditions improves. If the automobile is run on paved roads, its efficiency may be high because of the superior adhesion between the tires on the main wheels and the road. The automobile may turn out to be equally more effective on various types of soil surfaces since the tires mounted on the auxiliary wheels could be specially selected to suit soft soils. This could also be due to the fact that there are certain soils on which a vehicle with a high wheel loading is more effective.

*Variant II* (Fig. 95b). The auxiliary wheels in this model are of a much smaller diameter than the main wheels. Compared to the first variant, the vehicle configuration becomes superior and its mass reduces. The ability of the vehicle to cross ditches of a width equal to the distance between the extreme axles and the middle axles remains unaffected. However, the off-the-road mobility is adversely affected to some extent.

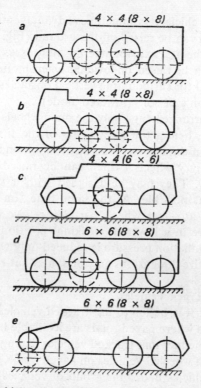

Fig. 95. Vehicles with a variable number of working wheels.

*Variant III.* Here the auxiliary wheels carry solid rubber tires with sharply defined lugs. In this, the overall reliability of the vehicle improves; since in the event of a breakdown of all its pneumatic tires, the automobile is still capable of motion. On some of the ice and snow covered surfaces and muddy dirt roads, its off-the-road mobility may be better than that of a vehicle in which only pneumatic tires are used. However, there are many other soil surfaces where such a vehicle may not be as effective as the one given in variant I.

When a vehicle with a $4 \times 4$ $(8 \times 8)$ arrangement is used with the auxiliary wheels in the lowered position, it is advisable to have all the main wheels as steering wheels to execute a turn.

In case the vehicle has a $6 \times 6$ arrangement, a successful negotiation of ditches is possible only with the help of the central axle (which may be raised or lowered); only the front axle can be used for steering (Fig. 95c). The automobile turns out to be comparatively simple. If the wheels used on the central axle are identical with those on the main axles, then there is no need to carry a spare wheel since the wheels on the middle axle could be utilized as spares.

For a four axled vehicle, it is sometimes advantageous to have the second axle as the one which can be raised off the ground (Fig. 95d). This makes it possible to use only the first axle for steering purposes.

Wheels which can be raised or lowered when mounted on the first axle (Fig. 95e) can be used for surmounting vertical obstacles (in the raised mode) and for locomotion on soft soils (lowered mode).

In all the above arrangements, only the main wheels are used for running on paved roads and, hence, the parameters of the tires mounted on these wheels are selected on the basis of load distribution on the main wheels only. Installation of auxiliary wheels (which can be raised or lowered) is used comparatively rarely. They may be designed with a smaller safety margin and made as light as possible. At the same time, on stretches with rough road conditions, the auxiliary wheels partially relieve the load on the main wheels when they are in a lowered (working) position. If variable inflation tires are used (their inflation pressure is reduced only when they are partially unloaded), then the tire dimensions may be somewhat reduced.

### Wheel and Crawler Track Vehicles

The opinion that it is better to use tracked vehicles where no roads exist and wheeled vehicles where paved roads are available has prevailed for a long time. Considering the fact that tracked vehicles damage the road surface and cannot compete with wheeled vehicles on paved roads, some researchers have classified tracked vehicles under the group of vehicles with restricted mobility. It is well-known that tracked vehicles have a shorter working life span. Naturally attempts were made to develop a combined wheel and track vehicle, which would combine the advantages of both types of vehicles, effectively operating on roads as well as off-the-road conditions with a sufficiently long period of service.

Figure 96 shows an automobile which has a wheel and track propelling device, with rubber and metal tracks directly mounted on the tires. The wheel drive in the track mode remains the same, as the driving force is transmitted from the pneumatic tires to the tracks only because of the adhesion between them. There is no need to install any kind of complicated transmission. The main difficulty encountered is during turning, which can be resolved on a quad-track automobile by utilizing an articulated body. Turning is effected by the relative turning of the articulated sections with respect to each other. It is also possible to turn the vehicle by employing different angular velocities for the wheels on the left and right hand side. The noteworthy feature in this arrangement is the difficulty in mounting and dismounting the tracks, which proves to be time consuming. Machines with propelling arrangements as these can be conveniently used on agricultural lands as wheeled vehicles during the dry season and as tracked vehicles during the spring, autumn and winter.

Fig. 96. The quad-track automobile with removable tracks.

There are also other well-known machines which have entirely independent tracks and wheels for locomotion. The presence of two propelling devices (each of which is designed for the total weight of the vehicle) and the arrangements for lowering or raising them makes the machine complicated and heavy. Such machines are, however, not in use at present.

A combination of tracks and wheels is highly advantageous when one of them acts as an auxiliary device for occasional use; in which case, it should be lighter in weight.

A combination of the main wheels of a vehicle with an auxiliary crawler track is shown in Fig. 97. This arrangement is similar to the wheeled arrangement with the wheels on the intermediate axles capable of being raised or lowered. However, for locomotion on soft soils, the auxiliary crawler track can be made far more effective than the use of auxiliary wheels. Considering the fact that the crawler track is only used for short durations, it should be made as light as possible. At the same time, the parameters of such a locomotion device can be so selected that, in most cases, the off-the-road mobility of the combined traction arrangement is better than that of a tracked vehicle. For instance, the use of long and sharp lugs on the crawler track is prohibited, since the track then becomes unsuitable for use on paved roads. However, this can be done in the case of auxiliary crawler tracks.

Fig. 97. An automobile with a set of main wheels and auxiliary crawler tracked wheels.

A combination of the three modes of locomotion, wheeled, wheel-and-track and tracked, for the wheel arrangement can lead to a performance of the highest versatility for a vehicle. However, in this case, the auxiliary crawler track has to be designed for the entire mass of the machine and a turning (cornering) provision made for the crawler track.

Compare a combined traction vehicle consisting of $4 \times 4$ main wheels and an auxiliary track with an $8 \times 8$ wheel arrangement. The mass of the wheel-and-track vehicle must be greater since the wheels are designed to carry double the load of the $8 \times 8$ arrangement, while the mass of the crawler track is not less than that of the two central axles. However, one must consider the fact that for the wheel-and-track vehicle, the dimensions of the tires can be somewhat reduced, since at low inflation pressures, they operate with only half the load. Highly complicated and expensive equipment for raising and lowering the crawler track, integrated with the suspension, replaces the usual four-wheel suspension. The transmission of a wheel-and-track locomotion device is similar to or even simpler than that of an $8 \times 8$ machine, since the power applied to the driving wheels of a crawler track is no more complicated than that provided to the second and third axles of an $8 \times 8$ wheel arrangement vehicle.

For wheel-and-track machines, steering must be controlled by the front and rear wheels; while for an $8 \times 8$ wheel machine, the first two axles along with an extremely simple steering gear could be used for steering. An $8 \times 8$ machine need not carry a spare wheel, while a wheel-and-track machine must definitely carry one.

It has been observed that a wheel-and-track machine has a large mass, is complex in construction is also expensive. However, the range of soil conditions over which it can operate does become considerably wider. Its off-the-road mobility on soft soils and soil surfaces, requiring long lugs, improves significantly. Simultaneously, there is an improvement in the performance of the machine on paved roads. This is because the parameters of the main wheels are so selected that they are closer to optimal for roads with a hard top dressing compared to an all-purpose $8 \times 8$ wheeled machine.

### Roller-and-Track Vehicles

The Airol (roller-track) tractor, which is a combination of pneumatic rollers and a crawler track (Fig. 98) holds considerable interest. In this machine, the pneumatic rollers carry out the function of the tracks. Chains, which mesh with the driving wheels, link the axles of the rollers at both ends. Roller supporters, which are normally provided in crawler tracked vehicles, are absent in this case. The chassis rests directly on the lower row's pneumatic rollers. When the driving wheel rotates, the chains displace the chassis relative to the rollers. This causes the chassis to move over the rollers, which are forced to roll over the road. The speed of the chassis relative to the road is double that of the rolling speed of the chains and the rotational speed of the rollers (Fig. 99b).

Fig. 98. Roller-track tractor.

While moving on yielding soils, the rollers sink into the ground. The rolling resistance of the rollers exceeds its normal limits, and they cease to roll. As a result, the chassis moves forward by sliding on the stationary rollers.

The external forces acting on the tractor are (Fig. 99): i) the components $G_a \cos \alpha$ and $G_a \sin \alpha$ of the gravitational force, ii) the wind resistance force, $W_w$, iii) the inertial force $G_a j$ as well as, iv) reactions $\Sigma T$ and $\Sigma Q$ from the soil.

The locomotion of the vehicle, governed by the roller-soil adhesion, is given by the inequality

$$G_a \left( \sin \alpha + \frac{j}{g} \right) + W_w = \Sigma T_i \leqslant G_a \phi \cos \alpha,$$

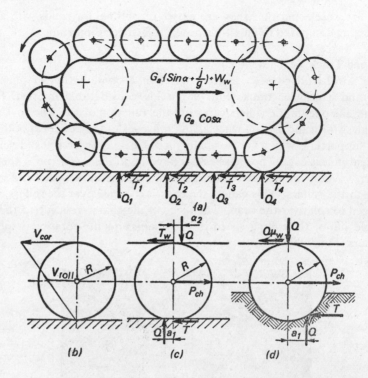

Fig. 99. Interaction between a roller-track tractor and the soil:

a—general arrangement; b—velocity diagrams; c—forces acting on the rollers for
the rolling motion of the chassis on the rollers; d—forces acting on the rollers for
chassis sliding over the rollers.

which in no way differs from the inequality for the usual wheeled machines.

The forces which act on the rollers so that the chassis moves forward as
they turn over the soil are shown in Fig. 99c. These are

$$P_{ch} = T + T_w;$$

$$(T_w - T) R = Q (a_1 + a_2),$$

where $P_{ch}$ is the tractive force of the chains;

$T$ is the tangential force acting between the rollers and the soil;

$T_w$ is the tangential force acting between the rollers and the chassis;

$Q$ is the normal reaction of the soil and the chassis on the rollers;

$a_1$ and $a_2$ are the displacements of the normal reactions caused by the rolling
losses between the soil and the rollers and the chassis and the
rollers.

Considering $\dfrac{a_1}{R} = f$ (where $f$ is the coefficient of the roller-soil rolling resistance) and $\frac{a_2}{R} = f_w$ (where $f_w$ is the roller-chassis rolling resistance), we have

$$T_w = T + Q\,(f + f_w);$$
$$P_{ch} = 2T + Q\,(f + f_w).$$

The tangential force $T_w$, transmitted from the chassis to the rollers, is greater than the tractive force $T$ due to the magnitude of the roller-soil and the roller-chassis rolling resistances. The driving force is the force of traction $T$. The tractive force of the chains exceeds force $T$ by more than double, which agrees with the kinematics of motion.

The maximum value of force $T_w$ is restricted by the friction force:

$$T_w \leqslant Q\mu_w$$

where $\mu_w$ is the coefficient of friction between the rollers and the chassis.

The maximum possible value of the tractive force developed by a single roller in the rolling mode is governed by the inequality

$$Q\,(\mu_w - f - f_w) > T < Q\phi.$$

The nature of operation of a roller-track tractor in the rolling mode is analogous to that of a multiwheeled vehicle. Hence, the conclusion drawn from the investigations for evaluation of the effect of the tire parameters and the number of axles on performance indices of multiaxled wheeled vehicles are applicable to this case.

The forces acting on the rollers, in case of the chassis sliding over the rollers, is shown in Fig. 99d:

$$P_{ch} = T + Q\mu_w;$$
$$(T - Q\mu_w)\,R = Q \cdot \alpha_1.$$

Substituting $\frac{a_1}{R} = f_1$ in the latter expression, we have

$$T = Q\,(\mu_w + f_1),$$

where $Qf_1$ is the soil resistance opposing the rolling motion of the rollers (the rollers have not as yet begun to roll) $f_1 \leqslant f$;

$f$ is the rolling resistance when the rollers roll over the soil.

In the case when $T \geqslant Q\,(\mu_w + f)$, the rollers slide over the chassis and roll over the soil in the reverse direction so that the chassis stays in place and locomotion is not possible.

Taking this into account, the maximum possible tractive force, developed by a single roller for the chassis sliding over the rollers, would be governed by the inequality

$$Q\,(\mu_w + f) > T < Q\phi.$$

Comparing the working of a roller-track tractor in the chassis sliding mode and those of wheeled or tracked vehicles, it may be noted that the maximum tractive effort due to adhesion for the roller-track tractor must be greater because of the greater adhesion between the soil and rollers. This is because a very large mass of soil is subjected to shear displacement (volumetric displacement). Almost all the force of adhesion between the vehicle and the soil may be realized as the tractive force ($T_{max} = Q\phi$), since the rollers neither rotate nor develop any ruts. In the case of wheeled or tracked vehicles, part of the adhesion force is lost in developing ruts

$$[T_{max} = Q \ (\phi - f_s)].$$

At the same time, the energy losses within the machine for the roller-track tractor are greater than those for wheeled or tracked vehicles. This is due to the greater frictional losses between the chassis and the rollers. Any measures taken to reduce the coefficient of friction between the chassis and the rollers ($\mu_w$) would not be desirable; since for locomotion on not-so-easily deformable soils, the maximum possible tractive force is restricted by the friction coefficient $\mu_w$.

Thus, the merit of the roller-track tractor lies in the fact that it can provide a much higher mobility over yielding soils (swamps, snow) compared to crawler tractors and, yet at the same time is capable of running on a paved road without damaging it. The disadvantages of this vehicle compared to a crawler tracked vehicle are: i) higher energy losses on locomotion, ii) poor efficiency on hard slippery and uneven surfaces, iii) poor climbing ability over obstacles in the path, iv) the larger size of the vehicle; and v) low maximum speed due to the absence of a cushioning effect for lack of springs and shock absorbers. Introduction of springs and shock absorbers makes the construction of the machine highly complicated.

### Wheeled Vehicles

A characteristic feature of the "Go-Devil" type of machine (Fig. 100) is that the longitudinal arms of the suspension, on which the wheels are mounted, may be rotated through 360° with respect to the machine chassis. The drive to the wheels and the suspension arms are all independent. When power is delivered to the wheels, the machine does not in any way differ from the usual wheeled machine. When the lever arms are rotated, the machine suspension displaces along a trajectory described by the arms.

Let us study the possibilities and economics of such a method of locomotion. In the present case, the limiting possibility of locomotion on a horizontal surface is not governed by the relationship between the possible tractive force and the resistance to motion, but only by the load bearing capacity of the soil. If the inertial forces are neglected (assume that the speed of locomotion is very small), the horizontal component of the wheel-soil interaction

Fig. 100. The "Go-Devil" automobile.

force is close to zero. This implies that the boundary conditions for motion are governed by the possible lift of the chassis above the soil during rotation of the lever arms of the suspension.

The interaction between the vehicle and the soil is represented in Fig. 101. Let us write down the equations for the components of the forces in $x$ and $z$ directions as well as for moments relative to point $O$:

$$T_1 + T_2 = m_a j \cos \alpha;$$

$$R_1 + R_2 = G_a + m_a j \sin \alpha;$$

$$R_2 L = G_a a + m_a j (h_g \cos \alpha + a \sin \alpha),$$

where $m_a$ is the mass of the automobile.

Substituting $a = \dfrac{L}{2} + l \sin \alpha$, the expression for $R_2$ is obtained as,

$$R_2 = \frac{1}{L} \left[ G_a \left( \frac{L}{2} + l \sin \alpha \right) + m_a j \left( h_g \cos \alpha + \frac{L}{2} \sin \alpha + l \sin^2 \alpha \right) \right].$$

For $\alpha = 90°$

$$R_2 = R_{max} = (G_a + m_a j) \left( 0.5 + \frac{l}{L} \right);$$

$$R_1 = R_{min} = (G_a + m_a j) \left( 0.5 - \frac{l}{L} \right);$$

$$\frac{R_{max}}{R_{min}} = \frac{0.5\,L + l}{0.5\,L - l}.$$

When the lever arms are in a horizontal position, the maximum vertical load acts on the wheels displaced towards the center of the chassis. An increase in the length of the arms leads to a large redistribution of the load on the axles. In the limiting case, when $l = \frac{L}{2}$; $R_{max} = G_a$ and $R_{min} = 0$. The condition for locomotion is $h < h_w$, where $h$ is the depth of sinkage of the wheels into the soil and $h_w$ is the road clearance.

The work done on locomotion is $A = G_a l\,(1 - \cos\alpha_0)$, where $\alpha_0$ is the initial angle of inclination of the lever arms. The path traversed by the chassis for one turn of the lever arms is

$$s = 2l\,\sin\alpha_0.$$

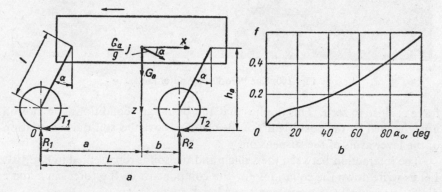

Fig. 101. Interaction between a "wheeled vehicle" and the road:

a—diagram of forces acting on the vehicle; b—relationship between the nominal coefficient of the resistance to motion and the initial angle of inclination of the lever arms.

The nominal coefficient of resistance to motion

$$f = \frac{A}{sG_a} = \frac{1 - \cos\alpha_0}{2\sin\alpha_0}. \tag{186}$$

Function $f = f(\alpha_0)$ is represented in Fig. 101b. The most probable value of the nominal coefficient of friction to motion for the method under study ranges between $f = 0.1$ and $f = 0.5$. This kind of locomotion is most uneconomical. However, it does have the capability of being able to pass over those yielding soils where ordinary wheeled vehicles are not able to move.

When the wheel sinkage in the soil is small, angle $\alpha_0$ approaches $\frac{\pi}{2}$. If it is not possible to move in the rolling mode, and it becomes necessary to drive the lever arms; then in order to obtain a smooth ride, the chassis may be displaced with the help of two levers. These are diagonally opposite to each other, while the other two levers are used for displacing the chassis in the following cycle. The chassis is raised and displaced by the front left and rear right levers, and the remaining lever arms are brought forward to prepare for the subsequent displacement of the chassis (they perform the idle portion of their movement). The smaller the angle $\alpha_0$, the greater is the idling angle of the lever arms ($\alpha_{idle} = \pi - \alpha_0$). When $\alpha_0 = \dfrac{\pi}{2}$, $\alpha_{idle} = \alpha_0 = \dfrac{\pi}{2}$ providing for a uniform rotation of the lever arms and the maximum displacement of the chassis per revolution of the lever arms ($s = 2l$). However, the work done on displacement is very large. When $\alpha_0$ is reduced, angle $\alpha_{idle}$ increases; the difference between the angular velocities of the lever arms during the working and idling modes of their operation and the corresponding inertia loads also increase. Under these circumstances, the displacement of the chassis per revolution of the lever arms reduces, but this is also accompanied by a reduction in the power required for displacement.

The expression for $f$ in equation (186) does not take into consideration the energy losses due to wheel sinkage into the soil. Considering the fact that the analysis of wheeled vehicles is only a preliminary one (qualitative), we shall assume the simplest linear relationship $G_w = ch$, where $c$ is a proportionality coefficient. In such a case, the resistance to motion, caused by the loss of energy in deforming the soil, would be proportional to the sinkage depth of the wheels into the soil and inversely proportional to the displacement of the chassis per revolution of the lever arms:

$$f_s = \frac{h}{2l \sin \alpha}; \quad f = \frac{1 - \cos \alpha_0}{2 \sin \alpha_0} + \frac{h}{2l \sin \alpha}. \tag{187}$$

When locomotion is accomplished by moving up an incline, force $G_a \sin \alpha$ acts parallel to the soil surface, where the wheel comes in contact with the soil. This force may lead to the skidding of the wheel over the soil or it may result in ground shear. In such cases, the possibility of locomotion is governed not only by the sinkage of the wheel into the soil but also by the resistance of the soil to shear.

If it is assumed that locomotion in the walking mode is used only on soil surfaces which are subject to severe deformation, then the likelihood of the wheel slipping or skidding on the soil surface is ruled out. Here the possible motion of the machine is governed by the load bearing capacity of the soil, when the load is applied at some inclination to the soil surface. The greater this angle, the smaller the load bearing capacity [see equation (78)].

For the above considered vehicle arrangement, displacement of the chassis by a simultaneous operation of all the lever arms leads to a discontinuous motion.

174

When the chassis is displaced by the action of two lever arms, the motion transfers the wheels to the next position without any pause. However, this greatly complicates the problem of providing stability to the chassis on two supports and doubles the load on them, resulting in greater sinkage into the soil.

In order to simultaneously provide a continuous displacement of the chassis on all the four wheels, a "multiroller wheel" vehicle is employed (Fig. 102). In principle, the nature of displacement of the chassis during rotation of the multiroller wheels is the same as in the previous case. When $n$ number of rollers are used on a single wheel, continuous motion is ensured for $\alpha_0 = \dfrac{\pi}{n}$.

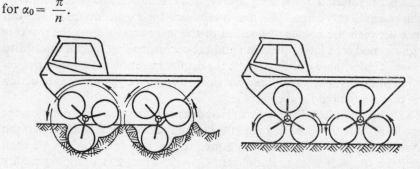

Fig. 102. The "Paddy Wagon" automobile (multiroller wheel vehicle).

Thus, when the number of rollers on the wheel is increased, the angle $\alpha_0$ decreases and, correspondingly, the vertical displacement of the chassis reduces as well as the energy expended on this motion. In the limiting case ($n$ tending to infinity), the multiroller wheel transforms into the usual wheel. When the number of rollers on a single wheel is increased, the volume of the soil undergoing deformation increases with a corresponding increase in the energy expended on this deformation. The horizontal component of the soil reaction increases (frontal resistance) when the roller is pressed into the soil. The mobility of the machine is adversely affected because of this. The construction of the vehicle becomes complicated, and the roller diameter becomes smaller.

In practice, one may use a three-roller wheel. A vehicle with such wheels provides a much smoother ride, a higher speed in the walking mode and lesser energy losses on the displacement of the chassis compared to the "Go-Devil" type of vehicle. Apart from this, this vehicle may be utilized as the usual wheeled type ($8 \times 8$ and $4 \times 4$). However, this machine becomes far more complicated and unwieldy than the "Go-Devil". The permissible diameter of the rollers is considerably smaller and its off-the-road mobility on soft soils is poor. Its ability to overcome various obstacles in the path is also considerably impaired.

A common disadvantage of wheeled vehicles is the difficulties encountered in providing the turning ability. The structural design for wheels that can be steered is quite difficult. The experimental wheeled vehicle "Go-Devil" (Fig. 100) consists of two sections joined together by a vertical pivot, which allows the turning of the sections relative to each other in the horizontal plane. Such a construction provides the turning ability for the machine through a hydraulic mechanism with a minimum turning radius of 5.5 m. This machine can travel on a severely rugged terrain. It can surmount obstacles of height up to 1.5 m and cross ditches of up to 1.8 m in width. It can maintain a horizontal position even while negotiating an incline of 40°. The self-weight of the machine is 3400 kg, and it can carry a load of 2200 kg. The machine size is $7600 \times 2280 \times 1220$ mm [55].

A wheeled vehicle with a three-roller wheel is illustrated by the experimental vehicle, "the Paddy Wagon", developed in the USA (Fig. 102). Experiments conducted on a (1/5)th scale model have shown that it can travel at high speeds on paved roads just like a wheeled vehicle and can freely move over mud, snow, swamps and sandy soils at relatively high speeds while traveling in the walking mode [55].

# CHAPTER 5

# Determination of the Principal Parameters of Off-the-road Vehicles

## CLASSES AND SYSTEMS OF DESIGN CALCULATIONS

During design and investigations of off-the-road automobiles, one comes across several classes of design calculations. These are:

1) determination of optimal parameters of the vehicle for given road-soil conditions;

2) verification of calculations to ascertain the off-the-road mobility and efficiency of utilization under various road-soil conditions for the automobile under design when the parameters of the machine have been selected on the basis of some other considerations;

3) verification of calculations to estimate the effectiveness of utilization of an existing automobile for certain specific soil conditions;

4) determination of the permissible load or working conditions for operation of an automobile at certain known parameters of the vehicle and specified soil conditions;

5) determination of the parameters of auxiliary equipment to enable the automobile to be used under difficult soil conditions.

The following calculation procedure may be recommended for the above described classification of design calculations:

i) selection of the system of design equations;

ii) selection of the design data for road-soil conditions;

iii) selection of empirical parameters (which cannot be derived by any analytical methods);

iv) selection of parameters for optimizing the vehicle and putting constraints on the other parameters;

v) design carried out on the basis of selected system of equations.

The preceding chapters describe equations from which all the above class of calculations can be carried out. These equations are presented in Table 12 in three design groups. The selection of a design system from among these three is governed by the ultimate aim of the design and the ingenuity of the designer.

Table 12

| System of design | Equations to be used |
|---|---|
| I | 14, 15, 41–43, 65, 67–71, 73, 78, 79, 142, 88, 90, 91, 93, 97, 100, 101, 118–120, 124 |
| II | 67, 100–102, 142, 108–111, 114–116, 118–120, 124 |
| III | 117, 142, 118–120, 124 |

The system I of design ensures the highest accuracy, by permitting the analysis of the greatest number of factors. However, computations carried out by this system are tedious and can be suitably handled by only an electronic computer. The system II provides a somewhat lower accuracy and allows fewer parameters to be analyzed in comparison with system I. The system III is the most simplified approach, where many gross approximations are introduced.

When calculations are carried out, according to any of the three classifications, first the magnitudes of several parameters are selected. The larger the number of such preselected parameters, the simpler the design procedure. The magnitudes of the empirical parameters are selected on the basis of the function of the automobile and the road-soil conditions derived from the statistical data available with the automobile and tire industries. For instance, while computing the parameters of tires for an off-the-road automobile designed for use in a wide variety of road-soil conditions, one may directly select the height of the lugs on the tread $\Delta_t$, the saturation coefficient of the tread pattern $m$, the fractional width $(b_t/B)$, and the fractional height $(h_t/H)$, utilizing the data presented in the section "The Effect of Wheel Parameters on Performance." In such a case, the tedium of calculations is greatly reduced. The number of parameters selected without prior computations depends upon the skill and resourcefulness of the designer as well as the accuracy desired.

In design calculations, the selection of parameters for optimization is of great importance. The solution to this problem is most easily obtained if it is related to the optimization of the vehicle with respect to a single parameter.

The parameters with respect to which a vehicle may be optimized are:

1) *Space occupied by the vehicle*. The calculations are aimed at providing the desired performance of the automobile for the minimum space occupied by it. In such a case, the minimum permissible values of the performance parameters are selected;

2) *Mass of the vehicle*. The aim of the design calculations is the same as in the previous case;

3) *The energy expended by the automobile in traversing the designed route*. Here the calculations must lead to the determination of such vehicle para-

meters, for which the energy expended on locomotion over the given route with various road and soil conditions at different sections, is a minimum;

4) *Maximum productivity of the automobile on a given route.* In this case, the vehicle parameters to be determined must ensure the transport of the maximum number of loads over a specified period.

The selection of any one of the above described parameters for optimization depends upon the function of the automobile. For instance, the fourth parameter is suitable for trucks and the third for passenger cars of constant mass.

In the case when design calculations are optimized with respect to any of the above parameters, there are certain restrictions placed on the dimensions of the tires ($D \leqslant D_{max}$; $B \leqslant B_{max}$; $d \geqslant d_{min}$), number of axles ($N_{min} < N \leqslant N_{max}$) and speed ($v_{min} < v < v_{max}$) etc. Further restrictions are placed on the basis of the engineering requirements of the automobile while taking its configuration into consideration.

## INITIAL DESIGN DATA FROM ROAD-SOIL CONDITIONS

In order to carry out all the above described types of design calculations, it is necessary to know the properties of the road and soil surfaces. A proper selection of the design parameters of the soil constitutes one of the most difficult problems because of the heterogeneity and instability of the soil surfaces, their insufficient study and the paucity of statistical data.

If the design computations are to be reliable, then it is necessary to know the following soil parameters: the modulus of deformation $E$, the thickness of the deformable soil layer $H_s$, the specific weight $\gamma$, the angle of (internal) friction $\phi_0$, the specific adhesion force of soil $c_0$, the modulus of shear $E'$ and the coefficient of friction between rubber and soil $\phi_r$.

For this it is necessary to have maps which depict the seasonal variation of the mechanical properties of the soil surfaces on a scale suitable for assessing soil properties over stretches equal to the wheel base. In the absence of such maps, one may utilize the averaged statistical data of the soils. However, in this case, accuracy is adversely affected. The averaged statistical data for the mechanical properties of different soil surfaces were given earlier.

The most complete data on the seasonal variation of the mechanical properties of soil were obtained for the proving grounds of the Automobile Road Institutes.

As an illustration of the seasonal variation of the mechanical properties of soils, Table 13 shows the data for clayey-loam soil surfaces of the steppe regions [12]. To determine the friction angle $\phi_0$ and the specific adhesion $c_0$ (not shown in Table 13), one may utilize the graphs plotted from statistical data (Fig. 103).

**Table 13**

| Type of soil (top dressing of road) | Parameters | | |
|---|---|---|---|
| | $W$ | $\gamma$, g/cm$^3$ | $E$, kg/cm$^2$ |
| Loose arable land: | | | |
| spring | 1.0 | 1.10 | 5 |
| summer | 0.35 | 1.20 | 20 |
| autumn | 0.65 | 1.15 | 10 |
| winter | 0.90 | 1.12 | — |
| Virgin land: | | | |
| spring | 0.90 | 1.20 | 20 |
| summer | 0.40 | 1.35 | 80 |
| autumn | 0.70 | 1.30 | 50 |
| winter | 0.85 | 1.20 | 800 |
| Compacted soil surface: | | | |
| spring | 0.68 | 1.35 | 60 |
| summer | 0.52 | 1.55 | 150 |
| autumn | 0.58 | 1.45 | 120 |
| winter | 0.65 | 1.25 | 600 |
| Dirt road: | | | |
| spring | 0.65 | 1.40 | 80 |
| summer | 0.50 | 1.55 | 150 |
| autumn | 0.55 | 1.45 | 120 |
| winter | 0.62 | 1.80 | 600 |

The coefficient of friction $\phi_r$ (between rubber and soil surface) is governed by the type and moisture content of the given soil (Table 14). Table 15 shows the mean design values of the soil surface parameters in the steppe regions. The magnitude of $E'$ may be estimated from the expression $E' = K_1 + K_2 c_0$, where $K_1 = 4$ kg/cm$^2$ and $K_2 = 20$; while the value of $a$ may be obtained from the equation

$$a = 1 + \frac{b}{H_s}.$$

In case sufficient statistical data for the mechanical parameters of the soil are not available, then they may be obtained by utilizing the method based on the relationship between the mechanical and physical properties of soils [72]. The physical parameters of the soils are determined with the help of soil maps and the statistical data of meteorological conditions. The procedure followed is: 1) the soil maps are acquired; and 2) based on the data provided by the Central Forecasting Institute [67] the reserves of the productive moisture content in the soils and the hydrological constants corresponding to the physical characteristics of the soils, are determined.

180

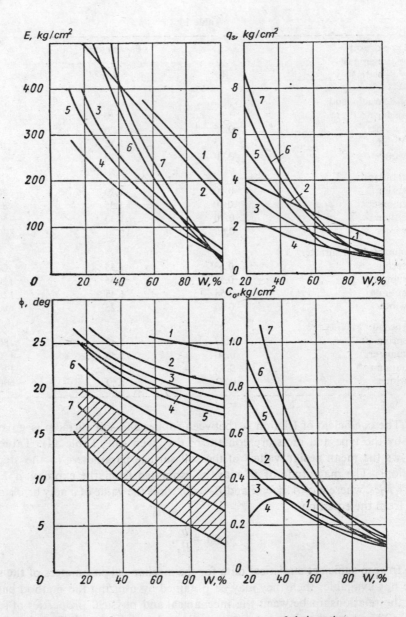

Fig. 103. Mechanical properties of soils as a function of their moisture content:

1—fine-grained sand; 2—light coarse-grained sandy loam; 3—light fine-grained sandy loam; 4—sandy loam; 5—light loam; 6—loam; 7—clay and heavy loam.

**Table 14**

| Type of soil (top dressing of road) | State | $\phi_1$ |
|---|---|---|
| Asphalt-metal dressing | Dry | 0.7–0.9 |
| | Wet | 0.4–0.6 |
| | Muddy | 0.25–0.45 |
| | Icebound | 0.1–0.2 |
| Cobbled paving | Dry | 0.5–0.7 |
| | Wet | 0.3–0.4 |
| Crushed stone and gravel covered | Dry | 0.5–0.7 |
| | Wet | 0.3–0.5 |
| | Muddy | 0.2–0.3 |
| Dirt road | Dry | 0.5–0.7 |
| | Wet | 0.2–0.4 |
| | Waterlogged | 0.15–0.25 |
| Sand | Dry | 0.3–0.5 |
| | Moist | 0.3–0.4 |
| Loam | Dry | 0.4–0.6 |
| | Plastic | 0.2 0.4 |
| | Viscous | 0.15–0.25 |
| Clay | Dry | 0.4–0.6 |
| | Plastic | 0.15–0.35 |
| | Viscous | 0,05–0.15 |
| Turf | With a sod cover | 0.1–0.2 |
| Snow | Loose: | |
| | dry | 0.2–0.3 |
| | wet | 0.1–0.2 |
| | Rolled | 0.1–0.2 |
| Ice | Smooth | 0.05–0.15 |

For a 0–50 cm thick soil layer, the following average hydrological constants are obtained: $\gamma$, g/cm³; the wilting coefficient $a_w$, %; field capacity $FC$, %.
The absolute humidity is obtained from the expression

$$w = \frac{10\,Y}{\gamma H_s} + a_w,$$

where $Y$ is the reserve of the productive moisture in mm.
The relative humidity is obtained as

$$w\% = \frac{w}{FC}\,100\%.$$

### Table 15

| Type of soil (top dressing of road) | Parameters | | | | | |
|---|---|---|---|---|---|---|
| | $\gamma$, g/cm³ | $E$, kg/cm² | $H_s$, cm | $c_0$, kg/cm² | $\phi_0$, deg | $\phi_r$ |
| **Loose arable land:** | | | | | | |
| spring | 1.1 | 5 | 35 | 0.08 | 7 | 0.1 |
| summer | 1.2 | 20 | 40 | 0.65 | 14 | 0.5 |
| autumn | 1.15 | 10 | 36 | 0.25 | 11 | 0.2 |
| winter | 1.12 | — | — | — | 7.5 | 0.15 |
| **Virgin land:** | | | | | | |
| spring | 1.2 | 20 | 26 | 0.1 | 7.5 | 0.1 |
| summer | 1.35 | 80 | 55 | 0.6 | 14.5 | 0.5 |
| autumn | 1.3 | 50 | 30 | 0.25 | 10 | 0.2 |
| winter | 1.2 | 800 | — | 0.15 | 9 | 0.2 |
| **Compacted soil surface:** | | | | | | |
| spring | 1.35 | 60 | 31 | 0.25 | 11 | 0.15 |
| summer | 1.55 | 150 | 60 | 0.45 | 12.5 | 0.6 |
| autumn | 1.45 | 120 | 32 | 0.4 | 12 | 0.2 |
| winter | 1.25 | 600 | — | 0.3 | 11 | 0.2 |
| **Dirt roads:** | | | | | | |
| spring | 1.4 | 80 | 32 | 0.3 | 11 | 0.15 |
| summer | 1.55 | 150 | 60 | 0.45 | 12.5 | 0.6 |
| autumn | 1.45 | 120 | 29 | 0.4 | 12 | 0.2 |
| winter | 1.8 | 600 | — | 0.35 | 11.5 | 0.2 |

3) Using the graphs (given in Fig. 103), the modulus of deformation $E$, the friction angle $\phi_0$ and the specific adhesion $c_0$ are determined from known values of the relative humidity and the type of soil.

By investigating the typical routes for a given class of automobile, from the soil maps, the frequency of running an automobile on various types of road and soil surfaces may be estimated.

For multipurpose off-the-road automobiles, designated for use in all parts of the country, it is better to utilize the experience of many years on such vehicles. The trial route may be distributed as follows:

1. Automobile roads: asphalt-cement top dressing—20%; cobble stone, gravel, broken stone (chips) top dressing—30%.

2. Dirt roads: dry level surface 5%; dry broken surface 5%; (sodden) wet 15%; snow covered and ice bound 10%; dry sandy surface 5%.

3. Off-the-road: 10%.

Some of the most difficult conditions which an off-the-road vehicle can negotiate are: dry sand of 40–50 cm thickness, wet (sodden) plowed fields of 25–30 cm depth, waterlogged meadows with a load bearing capacity of 0.5–0.7 kg/cm², virgin snow fields with a 50–60 cm snow cover and a density of 0.2–0.4 g/cm³, smooth ice.

The preliminary values of the mechanical parameters of the troublesome soil surfaces enumerated above are given in Table 16.

**Table 16**

| Soil surface | Parameters | | | | | | |
| --- | --- | --- | --- | --- | --- | --- | --- |
| | $\gamma$, g/cm³ | $E$, kg/cm² | $H_s$, cm | $\phi_0$, deg | $c_0$, kg/cm² | $\phi_r$ | $B$ |
| Dry sand | 1.5 | 20 | 50 | 32 | 0.01 | 0.3 | 0.015 |
| Sodden plowed field | 1.1 | 5 | 40 | 5 | 0.06 | 0.2 | 0.05 |
| Waterlogged meadow | 1.2 | 15 | 200 | 3 | 0.2 | 0.2 | 0.06 |
| Sodden dirt road | 1.3 | 10 | 25 | 12 | 0.05 | 0.2 | 0.04 |
| Virgin snow field | 0.25 | 1 | 60 | 16 | 0.03 | 0.1 | 0.02 |
| Ice | — | — | — | — | — | 0.15 | — |

## METHOD OF DETERMINING VEHICLE PARAMETERS

### Selection of the Vehicle Driving Mechanism and Tire Type

The design of a vehicle commences with the selection of the engine arrangement. This may be done either by the customer or by the organization building it. In both cases, the selection of the arrangement must be preceded by a careful technical and economic analysis.

It is advisable to carry out this task in two stages. During the course of the first stage, a rough layout of the vehicle must be decided upon, which would ensure that it is capable of carrying out all the tasks allocated to the automobile. For this, the results of the analysis of various arrangements of the driving mechanisms discussed earlier may be used.

The second stage consists of a comparative analysis of the selected arrangements for the purpose of choosing the most suitable one. This stage may be combined with the computation of the principal parameters of the wheels. The computational methods described earlier may be utilized to carry out a technical analysis of the selected arrangement. The economic analysis should be entrusted to specialists in the field.

During the preliminary selection of the vehicle arrangement, one should be guided by the following basic considerations:

1. The maximum load on the axles must conform to the load restrictions laid down by GOST 9314-59.

2. The dimensions of the vehicle must correspond to the limit of the maximum overall size. According to GOST 9314-59, the permissible overall size of an automobile is: width 2.5 m, height 3.8 m and length 12 m. A

tractor-trailer assembly with a semitrailer or a trailer may have a total length of 20 m.

3. Only four axled or wheel and track vehicles are capable of reliably negotiating ditches of more than 1 m width.

4. Increasing the number of axles complicates the construction of the automobile and increases its cost. The use of a combined traction device complicates the machine even more.

5. Adoption of a combined traction vehicle considerably increases the automobile's effective utilization on road-soil surfaces of varying properties.

6. While selecting the wheel arrangement, one must take into consideration the factory at which such an automobile could be produced.

Tires of a suitable type may be selected depending upon the automobile's functions, the road-soil conditions, the wheel arrangement as well as the capabilities of the tire manufacturing industry and the technical specifications of the various types of tires whose analysis has been discussed earlier.

### Example of Check Calculations of a System-II Vehicle

Determine the performance parameters of a $4 \times 4$ vehicle where $G_w = 1500$ kg; $B = 32$ cm; $H = 28$ cm; $b_t = B_F = 25$ cm; $D = 110$ cm; $h_t = 3$ cm; $\varDelta_t = 2$ cm; $m = 0.4$; $k_t = 0.35$ kg/cm$^2$; $t = 10$ cm; $h_w = 32$ cm; $\psi_1 = \psi_2 = 1$; $v = 100$ cm/sec; for use on a soil surface characterized by the parameters: $\gamma = 1.2$ (1.1–1.3) g/cm$^3$; $E = 10$ (5–15) kg/cm$^2$; $H_s = 20$ (30–10) cm; $\phi_0 = 10$ (5–15) degrees; $c_0 = 0.1$ (0.06–0.14) kg/cm$^2$; $\phi_r = 0.2$ (0.1–0.3); $E' = 2$ kg/cm$^2$; $B = 0.05$; $a = 1$. The values in parenthesis signify the permissible variation in the soil parameters.

1. Let us determine the vehicle's performance parameters for the average values of the soil parameters.

To simplify computations, let us first plot auxiliary graphs for $\delta = \delta\left(\dfrac{q}{p_w + k_t}\right)$ from equation (67), $h = h\,(q_d)$ from equations (102) and (142), $F = F\,(h, \delta)$ from equations (108)–(111). These are represented in Fig. 104.

Let us select four values of $q$ such as to cover the entire range of its possible values (0.85, 1.0, 1.2 and 1.6 kg/cm$^2$) and for each of them, the following operations for the front wheels of the vehicle shall be carried out:

determine $F = \dfrac{G_w}{q}$ and $q_d = \dfrac{q}{1 + \dfrac{Bvb_t}{F}}$;

determine $h$ from the curve $h = h\,(q_d)$ given in Fig. 104;

draw a horizontal line with an ordinate equal to $h$ to intersect the vertical line corresponding to $F$. From the point of intersection obtained, draw a line equidistant to the curve $h = h\,(F)$ until it intersects the abscissa. Draw a perpendicular at this point to intersect the curve $\delta = \delta\,(F)$ to obtain $\delta$;

From the curve $\delta = \delta\left(\dfrac{q}{p_w + k_t}\right)$, the value of $\dfrac{q}{p_w + k_t}$ is now obtained and, thereafter, the value of $p_w$;

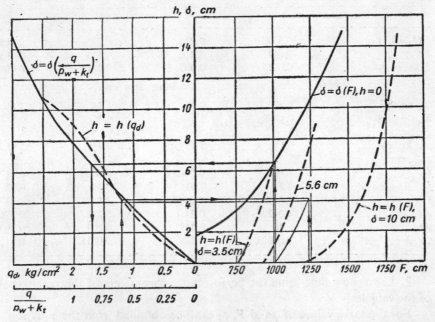

Fig. 104. Auxiliary graphs for check calculations.

from equations (71), (114) or (115), (100), (120), (116), (119) and (124), we shall successively determine the values of $b_{con}$; $f_s = \dfrac{Pf_s}{G_w}$; $f_t = \dfrac{Pf_t}{G_w}$; $f$; $\phi$ at $\delta_s = 0.3$; $\phi_T$; $\delta_s$ and $P_e$.

Let us tabulate these quantities

| Computed parameters | $q$, kg/cm$^2$ | | | |
|---|---|---|---|---|
| | 0.85 | 1.0 | 1.2 | 1.6 |
| 1 | 2 | 3 | 4 | 5 |
| For front wheels | | | | |
| $F$, cm$^2$ | 1770 | 1500 | 1250 | 938 |
| $q_d$, kg/cm$^2$ | 0.795 | 0.92 | 1.09 | 1.41 |
| $h_1$, cm | 2.25 | 2.7 | 3.8 | 5.6 |
| $\delta_1$, cm | 15 | 9.7 | 6.8 | 3.3 |
| $p_w$, kg/cm$^2$ | 0.22 | 0.5 | 0.98 | 2.5 |
| $b_{con}$, cm | 34.4 | 31.7 | 29.35 | 28 |
| $f_s$ | 0.026 | 0.033 | 0.052 | 0.095 |
| $f_t$ | 0.1 | 0.039 | 0.023 | 0.0154 |
| $f$ | 0.126 | 0.072 | 0.075 | 0.11 |

(Contd.)

| 1 | 2 | 3 | 4 | 5 |
|---|---|---|---|---|
| $\phi\,(\delta_s=0.3)$ | 0.270 | 0.249 | 0.225 | 0.188 |
| $\phi_T$ | 0.244 | 0.216 | 0.173 | 0.093 |
| $\delta_s\,(\phi_T=0)$ | 0.0055 | 0.00565 | 0.0148 | 0.0584 |
| | | For rear wheels | | |
| $q_d$, kg/cm² | 0.82 | 0.96 | 1.14 | 1.5 |
| $h_2$, cm | 0.15 | 0.3 | 0.4 | 0.7 |
| $\delta_2$, cm | 19 | 14 | 9 | 5 |
| $p_w$, kg/cm² | 0.14 | 0.35 | 0.73 | 1.95 |
| $b_{con}$, cm | 25 | 25 | 25 | 25 |
| $f_s$ | 0.002 | 0.0048 | 0.0076 | 0.0175 |
| $f_t$ | 0.2 | 0.08 | 0.03 | 0.02 |
| $f$ | 0.202 | 0.0848 | 0.0376 | 0.0375 |
| $\phi\,(\delta_s=0.3)$ | 0.262 | 0.24 | 0.215 | 0.176 |
| $\phi_T$ | 0.26 | 0.235 | 0.207 | 0.160 |
| $\delta_s$ | 0.00023 | 0.0003 | 0.0018 | 0.01 |

2. Let us now determine the performance parameters of the rear wheels of the vehicle:

For the same values of $q$ and $F$, $q_d$ shall be obtained from the equation

$$q_d = \frac{q}{1+\dfrac{Bvb_t}{2F}};$$

from the curve $h=h\,(q_d)$, we shall obtain the total depth of ruts $h_2'$, when both wheels have crossed, and also the depth of the rut developed by only the rear wheels $h_2=h_2'-h_1$;

just as in the case of the front wheels, the following parameters of the rear wheels are obtained:

$\delta_2$; $p_w$; $b_{con}$; $f_s$; $f_t$; $f$; $\phi$ at $\delta_s=0.3$; $\phi_T$; $\delta_s$ at $\phi_T=0$ and $P_e$.

3. The performance parameters for the entire vehicle shall now be determined.

Let us construct a graph for $f=f\,(p_w)$ and $\phi_T=\phi_T\,(p_w)$ for the front and rear wheels (Fig. 105). From this graph, the average values $f_{av}$ and $\phi_{T\,av}$ for various inflation pressures $p_w$ shall be determined. The expressions so obtained for $f_{av}=f_{av}\,(p_w)$ and $\phi_{T\,av}=\phi_{T\,av}\,(p_w)$ are the basic performance characteristics of the vehicle for the specified soil surface conditions.

Considering the fact that $\phi_T$ increases progressively with a decrease of inflation pressure $p_w$, let us determine the allowable limit to which $p_w$ can be reduced. For this purpose, a graph of the function $\delta_2=\delta_2\,(p_w)$ (Fig. 105) shall be constructed, from which the maximum allowable radial deformation for the given machine is 10 cm corresponding to $p_w=0.06$ kg/cm². This value of $p_w$ is the limiting inflation for the conditions specified in this case.

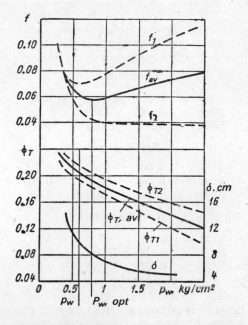

Fig. 105. Performance parameters of the vehicle as a function of inflation pressures.

From the curve $f_{av} = f_{av}$ ($p_w$), the optimal inflation pressure in the tires, from the rolling losses point of view, is obtained as $p_w = 0.8$ kg/cm². The traction characteristics of the vehicle shall be ascertained for this pressure.

The values of $q$, $q_d$, $F$, $f_s$ and $f$ are obtained by interpolation from the values tabulated earlier for the front and the rear wheels, corresponding to an inflation pressure of 0.8 kg/cm². These are tabulated below.

| Wheels | $q$, kg/cm² | $q_d$, kg/cm² | $F$, cm² | $L_w$, cm | $f$ | $f_s$ | $\tau_{max}$, kg/cm² |
|--------|-------------|---------------|----------|-----------|-----|-------|----------------------|
| Front  | 1.13        | 1.03          | 1320     | 53        | 0.071 | 0.045 | 0.25               |
| Rear   | 1.23        | 1.17          | 1040     | 42        | 0.037 | 0.008 | 0.26               |

Assuming $L_w = \dfrac{F}{b_t}$, let us obtain the values of $\phi$, $\phi_T$ and $P_e$ for $\delta_s$ equal to 0.02, 0.05, 0.1, 0.2, 0.4, 0.6 and 1.0 with the help of equations (116), (119) and (124). All these values are tabulated so that the traction efficiency characteristic of the vehicle can be plotted.

| Parameter | $\delta_2$ | | | | | | |
|---|---|---|---|---|---|---|---|
| | 0.02 | 0.05 | 0.1 | 0.2 | 0.4 | 0.6 | 1 |
| | | | Front wheels | | | | |
| $\phi$ | 0.066 | 0.113 | 0.15 | 0.178 | 0.197 | 0.206 | 0.22 |
| $\phi_T$ | 0.021 | 0.068 | 0.105 | 0.133 | 0.152 | 0.161 | 0.175 |
| $P_e$ | 0.073 | 0.078 | 0.09 | 0.122 | 0.217 | 0.418 | $\infty$ |
| | | | Rear wheels | | | | |
| $\phi$ | 0.053 | 0.096 | 0.132 | 0.165 | 0.185 | 0.194 | 0.202 |
| $\phi_T$ | 0.045 | 0.088 | 0.124 | 0.157 | 0.177 | 0.186 | 0.194 |
| $P_e$ | 0.039 | 0.0435 | 0.0545 | 0.085 | 0.180 | 0.37 | $\infty$ |
| | | | Complete vehicle | | | | |
| $\phi$ | 0.0595 | 0.104 | 0.141 | 0.171 | 0.91 | 0.2 | 0.211 |
| $\phi_T$ | 0.033 | 0.078 | 0.114 | 0.145 | 0.164 | 0.174 | 0.184 |
| $P_e$ | 0.056 | 0.06 | 0.072 | 0.103 | 0.199 | 0.394 | $\infty$ |

To determine the performance characteristics of the vehicle for the lower limits of the soil parameters, take the most difficult case, i.e. when each of the wheels rolls on virgin soil.

Taking the minimum value of $q=0.85$ kg/cm$^2$, $F=1770$ cm$^2$; $q_d=0.795$ kg/cm$^2$; $h=13.8$ cm; $\delta=9.15$ cm; $p_w=0.4$ kg/cm$^2$; $b_{con}=34.8$ cm; $f_s=0.127$; $f_t=0.031$; $f=0.158$ and $\delta_s=0.075$ is obtained.

The traction efficiency characteristic of the vehicle is tabulated below.

| $\delta_s$ | 0.075 | 0.1 | 0.3 | 0.5 | 0.7 | 1 |
|---|---|---|---|---|---|---|
| $\phi_T$ | 0 | 0.01 | 0.026 | 0.03 | 0.033 | 0.035 |
| $P_e$ | 0.17 | 0.176 | 0.226 | 0.317 | 0.527 | $\infty$ |

It can be seen that for extremely difficult tracts of the given soil surface, the traction coefficient does not exceed 0.035, for which the gradient that can be negotiated by the vehicle does not exceed 2°. The machine has no reserve capacity for its mobility. This is indicated by the value of $\phi_T$, which must not be less than 0.1.

## Example of the Direct Computation of Vehicle Parameters

Design the propelling device of an off-the-road automobile with a gross weight of 13000 kg, capable of negotiating ditches of up to 1.5 m width. The road-soil conditions correspond to the route map adopted for high off-the-road mobility automobiles (see the section on "Initial Design Data from Road-Soil Conditions").

To begin with, select the probable wheel arrangement of the vehicle and the type of tires to be used. Based on the restrictions placed on the axle loading of the given machine, a three or four axled arrangement appears to be suitable. Considering the fact that the machine must be capable of crossing ditches, the wheel arrangement could be 1–1–1, 1–2–1 or 1–1–1–1.

A vehicle equipped with variable inflation pressure tires and a detachable means of increasing adhesion or a combined traction device, comprising standard road tires with detachable tracks, would have been the most acceptable for given operating conditions. Thus, for an off-the-road machine of 13 tonnes weight, the possible variants are as follows:

Wheel arrangement 1–1–1 or 1–2–1 with variable inflation pressure tires. Such vehicles are used extensively, and their production does not involve any additional developmental work.

A 1–1–1 or 1–2–1 wheel arrangement vehicle, equipped with variable inflation pressure tires and replaceable treads or some detachable fitting for improving adhesion.

A 1–1–1–1 wheel arrangement vehicle with standard road tires and detachable tracks.

At present, production of the last three variants of vehicles has not been fully mastered. The design development of these vehicles first requires the solution of such problems as, for example, the manufacture of variable inflation pressure tires and detachable treads, development of detachable lugs, which can be easily mounted on variable inflation tires, and the ensuring of a reliable grip between the tires and the crawler tracks.

In order to select the optimum variant vehicle, it is necessary to determine the principal parameters of all the variants and carry out a comparative technical-economic analysis.

The profile width of various types of tires as a function of the nominal load is shown in Fig. 106. For standard road tires, $B = B(G_w)$ is well-defined without any noticeable scatter of the data points. For other types of tires, this functional relationship is not too well-defined and is characterized by a considerable scatter of the data points. This may be explained by the multiplicity of road-soil conditions for off-the-road tires and their insufficient study. The dimensions required for a tire increase with a decrease of the load bearing capacity and cohesive properties of soils. Hence, it is most advisable to determine the tire dimensions on the basis of the mechanical properties of the most yielding soils over which the vehicle has to pass and maintain its mobility.

## The Grapho-analytical Method of Determining Tire Parameters by System II

The vertical load on the wheel $G_w$ and two mechanical characteristics of the most yielding soil surface (such as a virgin snowfield) $q = q(h)$ and $\phi =$

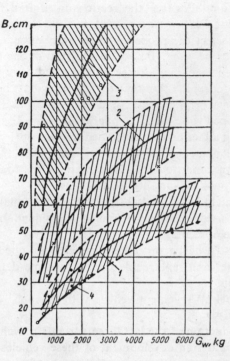

Fig. 106. Width of the tire profile as a function of nominal load:

1—variable inflation tire; 2—ribbed tire; 3—pneumatic-roller; 4—standard automobile tire.

$\phi(q)$, obtainable from equations (102) and (116), are used as initial parameters to obtain the required data. The aim of these calculations is to determine the minimum dimensions of the tires, which would ensure the desired mobility prescribed by the traction coefficient $\phi_T$. The most difficult conditions for locomotion are considered in this case, where each of the wheels moves in a new track (rut).

The calculation procedure is as follows:

1. The functional relationship $q = q(h)$ is plotted for several values of the tire profile width (width of rut) $B$ in the top right hand side of Fig. 107, using equation (102) and the parameters given in Table 16. It should be noted that for the maximum allowable deformation of the tires and the depth of the wheel ruts, not less than one-third of the height of the tire profile, the design width of the ruts, is approximately equal to its width. The value of $B$ is selected from the graph in Fig. 107. For $G_w = 1650$ kg, the width of the tire profile of an off-the-road vehicle is restricted to 30–70 cm. Taking this into consideration, width $B$ is selected as 30, 50 and 70 cm.

2. The function $\phi = \phi(q)$ at $\delta_s = 0.3$ is plotted in the upper left portion of Fig. 107 using equation (116).

3. The curve $f = f_s(h)$, for given values of $B$ equal to 30, 50 and 70 cm, is plotted with the help of expression $f_s = \dfrac{B}{G_w} \displaystyle\int_0^{h_1} q\,dh$ and the graphs $q = q(h)$. One may also utilize the simplified expression

$$f_t = \frac{q_{av}\,hB}{G_w},$$

for determining $f_s$. In this expression, $q_{av}$ is the average pressure over the range $h = 0$ to $h$ determined from the graph (Fig. 107).

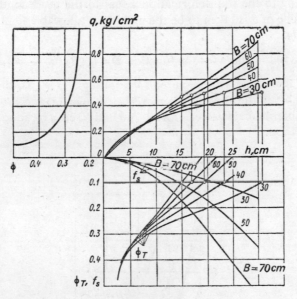

Fig. 107. Graphs for determining tire dimensions.

4. Let us now plot a graph of $\phi_T = \phi_T(h)$ for the selected values of $B$ using the curves $\phi = \phi(q)$, $q = q(h)$ and $f_s = f_s(h)$. For instance, take $B = 30$ cm and $h = 15$ cm. For these values, from the curves in Fig. 107, we obtain $q = 0.36$ kg/cm², $\phi = 0.3$ and $f_s = 0.06$. Let us determine $\phi_T = \phi - f_s = 0.24$ and obtain a point in the lower right hand side of Fig. 107 with its coordinates of $\phi_T = 0.24$ and $h = 15$ cm.

5. Let us draw a horizontal line with the ordinate equal to $\phi_T = 0.1$ in the lower right hand quadrant of Fig. 107, corresponding to the desired off-the-road mobility. From the point of intersection of this line with the curve $\phi_T = \phi_T(h)$, draw a vertical line till it intersects the curve $q = q(h)$, thus obtaining

192

$B$, $h$ and $q$ for which $\phi_T = 0.1$. For instance, for $B = 70$ cm, $h = 15$ cm and $q = 0.47$ kg/cm².

6. For each of the selected values of $B$, the value of $D$ is obtained from the expression

$$D = \left\{ \frac{2G_w}{\pi q B \left[ (1 - \zeta_z) \sqrt{\delta} + \zeta_z \sqrt{\delta + h} \right]} \right\}^2. \tag{190}$$

Equation (190) is derived from equation (111). Here it is assumed that the ruts are rectangular in the cross section with a width $B$ and $b_t \approx b_w \approx B$, $l = \sqrt{D\delta}$, $L = \sqrt{D(\delta + h)}$, $\zeta_z = \frac{2}{3} \cdot \frac{q_{h/2}}{qh}$, where $q_{h/2}$ is the pressure corresponding to the soil deformation equal to half the depth of the ruts; $q_h$ is the pressure corresponding to the soil deformation equal to the total depth of the ruts. The magnitude of $\delta$ is taken to be the maximum allowable for the tires ($\delta_{max} = 0.3$–$0.35H$).

7. Let us plot a curve for the function $D = D\,(B)$ for $\dfrac{H}{B} = 1$, as shown in Fig. 108. If more points are required for plotting $D = D\,(B)$, then these may be obtained by plotting additional curves for $\phi_T = \phi_T\,(h)$ and $q = q\,(h)$, in Fig. 107 for the intermediate values of $B\,(B = 40$ and $60$ cm), by adopting the interpolation method.

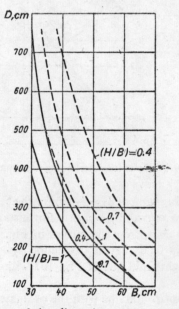

Fig. 108. The combination of tire dimensions which would provide the desired mobility of a vehicle:

full lines—$G_w = 1650$ kg; broken lines—$G_w = 2170$ kg.

8. The magnitude of $D$ is obtained from equation (190) and curve $D = D(B)$ is plotted for the wide profile $\frac{H}{B} = 0.7$ and ribbed $\frac{H}{B} = 0.4$ tires (see Fig. 108).

The curves shown in Fig. 108 represent all possible combinations of tire dimensions $(B, H, D)$, which would ensure that, for deformation $\delta = 0.3\ H$, the traction coefficient $\phi_T$ is 0.1. The designer selects the most suitable combination from among these to satisfy the functional requirements of the vehicle and special features of its design. Apart from this, other conditions to be satisfied are those relating to the restrictions placed on the outer diameter of the tires and their width based on the configuration of the vehicle, the minimum allowable diameter of the wheel rim, necessary for accommodating the braking and other mechanisms, the feasibility of using tires and wheel rims manufactured by the industry, and the nature of influence of the outer diameter width and shape of the profile of tires on the performance of the automobile.

Let us take the minimum volume of the tire as the optimization parameter

$$V_t = 2\pi BH\,(D-H)N. \qquad (191)$$

Figure 109 shows the functional relationship $V_t = V_t\,(B)$ for a vehicle with 1–2–1 and 1–1–1 wheel arrangement. In all cases, the volume occupied by the tires reduces when the tire profile width is increased along with a corresponding decrease of its diameter. Hence, it is advisable to use the minimum possible diameter for the wheel rim in conformity with the layout of the vehicle.

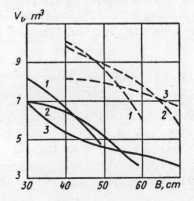

Fig. 109. Volume occupied by tires of a vehicle as a function of the width of the tire profile.

$1-\dfrac{H}{B}=1$;  $2-\dfrac{H}{B}=0.7$;  $3-\dfrac{H}{B}=0.4$. Solid curves—scheme for vehicle with 1–2–1 wheel arrangement; Broken curves—scheme for vehicle with 1–1–1 wheel arrangement.

Taking the minimum ratio $\dfrac{D}{H} = 2.6$, the following minimum tire dimensions are obtained for the 1–2–1 wheel arrangement vehicle: $D=1300$ mm and $B=480$ mm for variable inflation pressure tires; $D=1040$ mm and $B=585$ mm for wide-profile tires and $D=1000$ mm and $B=700$ mm for ribbed tires. As far as the volume occupied by the tires is concerned, the wide-profile tires and the ribbed tires are identical. However, the wide-profile tires are preferable because of their greater versatility and superior performance on paved roads. Variable inflation pressure tires also provide a very high degree of versatility, but in the present case (for the 1–2–1 wheel arrangement), the volume occupied by them is 20% more than that of the wide-profile tires.

For the 1–1–1 wheel arrangement vehicle, both from consideration of the volume occupied by the tires and their off-the-road mobility, variable inflation pressure tires $\left(\dfrac{H}{B} = 1\right)$ 1400–590 are found to be the best. The total volume occupied by the tires for the 1–1–1 wheel arrangement vehicle is almost 50% more than that for the 1–2–1 vehicle.

Among the various tires manufactured by the tire industry, the tire which comes close to satisfying the requirements of the 1–2–1 wheel arrangement vehicle is the variable inflation tire 16.00–20 ($D=1390$ mm, $B=438$ mm) and the wide-profile tire ($1100 \times 520$–508); while for the 1–1–1 wheel arrangement vehicle, the most suitable one is the variable inflation tire 18.00–24 (1600–555).

### Computation of Tire Inflation Pressure

While determining tire dimensions, the magnitude of contact pressure was obtained for the most yielding soil conditions. The minimum pressure is obtained from the graph shown in Fig. 107 for tires 1040–585 as $q_{min}=0.48$ kg/cm$^2$. Using the expression

$$q_{min} = p_{w\ min} + k_t,$$

the value of $p_{w\ min}$ can be determined.

From the statistical data, it is seen that $k_t = (0.1$–$0.15)\ p_{w\ max}$. When running on paved roads, the value of $p_w$ is a maximum for which the relative deformation of wide-profile tires $\delta_{min} \approx 0.14\ H$.

Since $k_t = 0.1\ p_{w\ max}$ and $\delta_{min} = 0.14\ H$, using equations (67) and (111), the expression for maximum pressure is obtained as

$$p_{w\ max} = \frac{1.15\ G_w}{b_t\ \sqrt{(D-0.14H)\ 0.14H}\left[3.05 - \left(1.75 - \dfrac{0.14\ Hc_t}{b_t}\right)^2\right]}. \tag{192}$$

For the present case, $G_w = 1650$ kg; $D=104$ cm; $H=41$ cm; $B_F = b_t = 50$ cm; $B = 58.5$ cm; $p_{w\ max} = 1.75$ kg/cm$^2$; $k_t = 0.175$ kg/cm$^2$; $p_{w\ min} = 0.3$ kg/cm$^2$.

**Determination of Vehicle Parameters on an Electronic Computer**

When the parameters of a vehicle are to be determined with the help of an electronic computer, it is advisable to utilize the equations grouped under system I. The parameter selected for optimization in this case could be any of the four parameters given earlier.

Consider the case where the vehicle parameters are optimized for the minimum work done in negotiating a given route.

The work done is defined by $P_{e\ av}$, which is obtained from equation (124).

For an off-the-road automobile, one may select a design route corresponding to a particular distribution of road-soil surface conditions as described in the section "Initial Design Data from Road-Soil Conditions".

In accordance with the specific duty of the machine, the following restrictions may be imposed:

for desired off-the-road mobility ($\phi_T \geqslant \phi_{T\ av}$),

for permissible dimensions of tires ($D < D_{per}$, $B < B_{per}$, $d \geqslant d_{per}$),

for permissible number of axles ($N_1 < N < N_2$).

All the tire parameters are expressed in terms of $B$ using the following relationships:

$$H = v_w B;$$

$$U = B(1.8\ v_w + 0.82);$$

$$h_t - 0.1B;$$

$$b_t = B(1.02 - 0.2\ v_w);$$

$$R = v_w B + \frac{kG_w}{B}\ (k \approx 1\ \text{cm}^2/\text{kg}).$$

The calculation procedure is as follows:

1. Select value of $v_w$ and $N$ based on an analysis of road-soil conditions and the preliminary layout assumed for the vehicle (for instance, $v_w = 1$, $N = 4$).

2. Select 4–5 values of $B$, uniformly distributed over the range, $B = B_{per}$ to $B = B_{p.r}$ ($B_{p.r}$ is the width of the tire profile for running on paved roads, obtained from curve 4, Fig. 106).

3. For each of the assumed values of $B$, determine $P_e$ with the help of the set of equations of system I for each portion of the route and the value of $P_{e\ av}$ from equation (124).

4. From the functional relationship $B = B(P_{e\ av})$ so obtained, determine the value of $B_{opt}$ corresponding to $P_{e\ av\ min}$.

5. To improve the accuracy of the optimal parameters of the vehicle, repeat the calculations (points 1–4) for other possible variants of the vehicles and types of tires (for instance, for $v_w$ equal to 0.4 and 0.7; $N$ equal to 2 or 3).

From the expressions obtained i.e., $v_w = v_w (P_{e\ av})$ and $N = N (P_{e\ av})$, determine the optimal values of $v_w$ and $N$, corresponding to the minimum value of $P_{e\ av}$.

6. Determine the optimal value of the tread parameters. For $B = B_{opt}$; $v_w = v_{w\ opt}$; $N = N_{opt}$ repeat the calculations (points 1 to 4) for several values of $m$, $t$, $b_t$, $r_t$, $\Delta_t$ and from the expressions so obtained for $m = m (P_{e\ av})$, $t = t (P_{e\ av})$, $b_t = b_t (P_{e\ av})$, $r_t = r_t (P_{e\ av})$ and $\Delta_t = \Delta_t (P_{e\ av})$, determine the optimal values of $m$, $t$, $b_t$, $r_t$ and $\Delta_t$.

# References

1. Ageikin, Ya.S. 1959. Issledovanie raboty shin peremennogo davleniya na deformiruemom grunte (Investigation of the working of variable inflation tires on deformable soils). In Sb: *Problemy Povysheniya Prokhodimosti Kolesnykh Mashin*, Izd. AN SSSR, Moscow.
2. Babkov, V.F., A.K. Birulya and V.M. Sidenko. 1959. Prokhodimost' kolesnykh mashin po gruntu (Off-the-road mobility of wheeled machines on soil). Avtotransizdat, Moscow.
3. Bezborodova, G.B. and N.F. Kosharnyi. 1966. E'ksperimental'noe issledovanie stsepleniya shin s gruntom pri buksovanii (Experimental investigation of tire-soil adhesion during skidding). *Avtomobil'naya Promyshlennost'*, No. 4.
4. Biderman, V.L., et al. 1963. Avtomobil'nye shiny (Automobile tires). Goskhimizdat, Moscow.
5. Birulya, A.K. 1959. Issledovanie vzaimodeistviya koles s poverkhnost'yu kacheniya kak osnova otsenki prokhodimosti (Investigation of the interaction between wheels and the rolling surface as a basis for evaluating off-the-road mobility). In Sb: *Problemy Povysheniya Prokhodimosti Kolesnykh Mashin*, Izd. AN SSSR, Moscow.
6. Bocharov, N.F., et al. 1964. Issledovanie deformatsii e'lementov rezino-kordnoi obolochki pnevmokatkov (Investigation of the deformation of rubber-cord casing elements of pneumatic-rollers). *Izvestiya Vuzov SSSR. Mashinostroenie*, No. 7.
7. Bocharov, N.F., et al. 1968. Vliyanie shaga gruntozatsepov na stsepnye kachestva dvizhitelya s nizkimi, ravnomerno raspredelennymi davleni-yami v kontakte s gruntom (Influence of the spacing of lugs on the adhesion properties of vehicles with a low, uniformly distributed pressure at the surface of contact with the soil). *Izvestiya Vuzov SSSR. Mashinostroenie*, No. 2.
8. Buvert, V.V., et al. 1960. Sukhoputnyi transport lesa (Overland transport of timber). Goslesbumizdat, Leningrad.
9. Velikanov, D.P. 1962. E'kspluatatsionnye kachestva avtomobilei (Performance of automobiles). Avtotransizdat, Moscow.
10. Vol'skii, S.G., et al. 1966. Metodika e'ksperimental'nogo issledovaniya oporno-stsepnykh kachestv kolesnykh dvizhitelei pri malykh skorostyakh (Experimental investigation of the bearing-adhesion quality of wheeled

vehicles at low speeds). In Sb: *Avtomobil'nyi Transport*, No. 3, Tekhnika, Kiev.

11. Govorushchenko, N.Ya. 1964. Voprosy teorii e'kspluatatsii avtomobilei na dorogakh s razlichnoi stepen'yu rovnosti pokrytii (Problems related to the theory of operation of automobiles on roads with top dressings of different smoothness). Izd. KhGU.

12. Golovanenko, S.L. and V.M. Sidenko. 1959. Issledovanie soprotivleniya dvizheniyu pnevmaticheskikh koles v zavisimosti ot sostoyaniya grunta (Investigation of resistance to the motion of pneumatic wheels as a function of the state of the soil). *Trudy KhADI*, Vol. 20, Izd. KhGU.

13. Gol'd, B.V. 1962. Konstruirovanie i raschet avtomobilya (Construction and design of automobiles). Mashgiz, Moscow.

14. Grinchenko, I.V., et al. 1967. Kolesnye avtomobili vysokoi prokhodimosti (Wheeled automobiles of high off-the-road mobility). *Mashinostroenie*, Moscow.

15. Gus'kov, V.V. 1966. Optimal'nye parametry sel'skokhozyaistvennykh traktorov (Optimal parameters of agricultural tractors). *Mashinostroenie*, Moscow.

16. Zadorozhnyi, V.I. 1966. Pokazateli tyagovo-stsepnykh kachestv mnogokolesnogo dvizhitelya (Traction-adhesion indices of multiwheeled vehicles). In Sb: *Avtomobil'nyi Transport*, No. 2, Tekhnika, Kiev.

17. Zakharov, S.P. and V.I. Novopol'skii. 1957. Raspredelenie udel'nogo davleniya shiny na dorogu pri vysokikh skorostyakh (Specific pressure distribution of tires on roads at high speeds). In Sb: *Metody Rascheta i Ispytaniya Avtomobil'nykh Shin*, Goskhimizdat, Moscow.

18. Kazarnovskii, V.D. 1961. Stepen' uplotneniya grunta i ego soprotivlenie sdvigu (The extent of soil compaction and its shear resistance). *Avtomobil'nye Dorogi*, No. 12.

19. Klenin, N.I. 1960. Issledovanie protsessa smyatiya pochvy tverdymi telami (Investigation of the crushing process of soils by solid bodies). Sel'khozgiz, Moscow (*Trudy MIMESKh*, Vol. 12).

20. Knoroz, V.I. 1960. Rabota avtomobil'noi shiny (Working of automobile tires). Avtotransizdat, Moscow.

21. Knoroz, V.I. and A.S. Shelukhin. 1960. Momenty inertsii avtomobil'nykh koles (Moments of inertia of automobile wheels). *Avtomobil'naya Promyshlennost'*, No. 9.

22. Knoroz, V.I. and A.M. Khlebnikov. 1960. O nagruzke na arochnye shiny i ikh oboda (The influence of the load on ribbed tires and their wheel rims). Izd. NAMI, Moscow (*Trudy NAMI*, Vol. 12).

23. Knoroz, V.I., et al. 1968. Vliyanie soprotivleniya kacheniyu shin na raskhod topliva avtomobilem (The influence of the rolling resistance of tires on fuel consumption of automobiles). *Avtomobil'naya Promyshlennost'*, No. 3.

24. Komissarova, V.A. 1960. Metodika otsenki prokhodimosti gruntovykh dorog dlya avtotransporta lesnoi promyshlennosti (Method of evaluating the off-the-road mobility on dirt roads for transport of forest produce by automobile). Goslestekhizdat, Moscow (*Trudy TsNIIME'*, *XV*, Vol. 4).

25. Korotonoshko, N.I. 1957. Avtomobili vysokoi prokhodimosti (The high off-the-road mobility of automobiles). Mashgiz, Moscow.

26. Korotonoshko, N.I. 1960. Kratkii analiz printsipial'nykh skhem dvizhitelei dlya bezdorozh'ya po rezul'tatam e'ksperimental'nykh rabot NAMI (A short analysis of the principal arrangements of locomotion devices for off-the-road conditions based on experimental results of NAMI). Izd. NAMI, Moscow (*Trudy NAMI*, Vol. 19).

27. Korotonoshko, N.I. and S.A. Shuklin. 1968. Vliyanie konstruktsii shin i samoblokiruyushchikhsya differentsialov na prokhodimost' avtomobilya URAL-375 (Influence of tire design of self-locking differentials on the off-the-road mobility of automobiles URAL-375). *Avtomobil'naya Promyshlennost'*, No. 7.

28. Korchunov, S.S. 1948. Nesushchaya sposobnost' i deformatsiya nizinnoi torfyanoi zalezhi (Bearing capacity and deformation of lowland turf beds). Gosenergoizdat, Moscow-Leningrad (*Trudy VNIITP*, Vol. I).

29. Kosharnyi, N.F. and Obolenskii, N.N. 1968. Vliyanie srednego udel'nogo davleniya na koe'ffitsient stsepleniya shin s gruntom (Influence of mean specific pressure on the tire-soil adhesion coefficient). In Sb: *Avtomobil'nyi Transport*, Vol. 5, Tekhnika, Kiev.

30. Krzhivitskii, A.A. 1949. Snegokhodnye mashiny (Snowmobiles). Mashgiz, Moscow.

31. Krestovnikov, G.A. 1964. O soprotivlenii dvizheniyu avtomobilei (Resistance to automobile locomotion). *Avtomobil'naya Promyshlennost'*, No. 6.

32. Kulikov, N.K. 1955. Rabota avtomobil'nogo kolesa (Working of automobile wheels). Mashgiz, Moscow.

33. Lazebnikov, M.G. and Yu.L. Bakurevich. 1966. E'kspluatatsiya avtomobilei v tyazhelykh dorozhnykh usloviyakh (Operation of automobiles under difficult road conditions). *Transport*, Moscow.

34. Lanin, V.I. 1955. Kachenie vedushchego kolesa s e'lastichnoi shinoi (Rolling of a driving wheel fitted with an elastic tire). In Sb: *Avtomobil'*, No. 61, Ed. A.A. Lipgart, Mashgiz.

35. Lipman, G.I. and G.M. Turgenev. 1965. Snegokhody (Snowmobiles). *Znanie*, Moscow.

36. Litvinov, A.S., et al. 1963. Shassi avtomobilya (Automobile chassis). Mashgiz, Moscow.

37. Marshak, A.L. 1956. O profile poverkhnosti pnevmaticheskikh koles pri kontakte ikh s pochvoi (The surface profile of pneumatic tires on contact with soil). *Sel'skokhozyaistvennaya Mashina*, No. 3.

38. Maslov, N.N. 1949. Prikladnaya mekhanika gruntov (Applied soil mechanics). Mashstroiizdat, Moscow.
39. Nadezhdii, G.V. 1966. Vliyanie shiriny oboda na iznos protektora shiny (Effect of wheel rim width on tread wear). *Avtomobil'naya Promyshlennost'*, No. 4.
40. Nafikov, M.Z. and I.S. Polyakov. 1968. Raschet soprotivleniya dvizheniyu traktora (Computation of resistance to tractor motion). *Traktory i Sel'-khozmashiny*, No. 1.
41. Novichikhin, V.A. 1964. Deformatsiya opornymi poverkhnostyami szhimaemoi sredy (The deformation of bearing surfaces of compressible substances). *Vysshaya Shkola*, Minsk.
42. Novopol'skii, V.I. and O.B. Tret'yakov. 1963. Issledovanie proskal'zyvaniya e'lementov risunkov protektora v zone kontakta avtomobil'nykh shin (Investigation of the slippage of tread pattern elements in the contact zone of automobile tires). *Kauchuk i Rezina*, No. 11.
43. Novopol'skii, V.I. 1960. Soprotivlenie avtomobil'nykh shin kacheniyu pri vysokikh skorostyakh (Rolling resistance of automobile tires at high speeds). *Avtomobil'naya Promyshlennost'*, No. 10.
44. Ornatskii, N.P. 1959. Raspredelenie nagruzki mezhdu osyami povozki, rasstanovka ee shin i soprotivlenie kacheniyu povozki po rykhlomu gruntu (Load distribution between the axles of a vehicle, arrangement of its tires and the rolling resistance of the vehicle over loose soil). In Sb: *Problemy Povysheniya Prokhodimosti Kolesnykh Mashin*, Izd. AN SSSR, Moscow.
45. Petrov, I.P. and V.I. Knoroz. 1965. O raspredelenii davlenii v kontakte shiny s opornoi poverkhnost'yu (On the pressure distribution at the contact between tires and the bearing surface). Izd. NAMI, Moscow (*Trudy NAMI*, Vol. 79).
46. Petrushov, V.A. 1965. Obobshchennyi metod rascheta soprotivlenii kacheniyu avtomobilei i avtopoezdov s razlichnymi tipami privoda (A generalized computation method for determining the rolling resistance of automobiles and tractor-trailers with various types of drives). Izd. NAMI, Moscow (*Trudy NAMI*, Vol. 76).
47. Pirkovskii, Yu.V. 1965. Nekotorye voprosy kacheniya avtomobil'nogo kolesa (Some problems of automobile wheel rolling). *Avtomobil'naya Promyshlennost'*, No. 12.
48. Pokrovskii, G.I. 1941. Trenie i stseplenie v gruntakh (Friction and cohesion of soils). Stroiizdat, Moscow.
49. Poletaev, A.F. 1963. Kachenie vedomogo kolesa (The rolling of driven wheels). *Traktory i Sel'skokhozyaistvennye Mashiny*, No. 2.
50. Poletaev, A.F. 1964. Kachenie vedushchego kolesa (The rolling of driving wheels). *Traktory i Sel'skokhozyaistvennye Mashiny*, No. 1.
51. Poletaev, A.F. and N.I. Glagolev. 1967. K voprosu ob opredelenii koe'-

ffitsientov uprugosti i vremeni relaksatsii pochvy (The problem of determining the coefficients of elasticity and relaxation time of soils). *Avtomobil'naya Promyshlennost'*, No. 8.

52. Razorenov, V.F. 1963. O nekotorykh zakonomernostyakh izmeneniya mekhanicheskikh svoistv vodonasyshchennykh glinistykh gruntov (Laws governing the variation of mechanical properties of watersaturated clayey soils). *Osnovaniya, Fundamenty i Mekhanika Gruntov*, No. 3.

53. Rokas, S.I. 1965. Opredelenie osnovnykh parametrov gruntov s tsel'yu otsenki tyagovo-stsepnykh kachestv avtomobilei (Determination of the principal parameters of soils with the aim of evaluating the traction-adhesion qualities of automobiles). *Avtomobil'naya Promyshlennost'*, No. 1.

54. Saakyan, S.S. 1959. Vzaimodeistvie vedomogo kolesa i pochvy (Interaction between a driving wheel and the soil). Izd. Ministerstva Sel'skogo Khozyaistvo Armyanskoi SSR, Erevan.

55. Selibanov, I.I. 1967. Avtomobili i transportnye gusenichnye mashiny vysokoi prokhodimosti (Automobiles and high mobility crawler-tracked transport machines). Nauka, Moscow.

56. Semenov, V.M. and R.G. Armaderov. 1962. Rabota gruzovogo avtomobilya v tyazhelykh dorozhnykh usloviyakh (Operation of trucks under difficult road conditions). Avtotransizdat, Moscow.

57. Smirnov, G.A. 1965. Vliyanie chisla i raspolozheniya osei na tyagovostsepnye kachestva polnoprivodnykh avtomobilei (Influence of the number and disposition of axles on the traction-adhesion properties of all wheel driven automobiles). *Avtomobil'naya Promyshlennost'*, No. 12.

58. Sokolova, V.A. et al. 1962. Issledovanie vzaimodeistviya arochnogo kolesa s opornoi poverkhnost'yu (Investigation of the interaction between a ribbed-tire wheel and the bearing surface). Izd. NAMI, Moscow (*Trudy NAMI*, Vol. 54).

59. Sokolovskii, V.V. 1954. Statika sypuchei sredy (Statics of friable materials). Gosstroiizdat, Moscow.

60. Sokolovskii, V.V. 1950. Teoriya plastichnosti (Theory of plasticity). Gostekhizdat, Moscow.

61. Terzaghi, K. 1961. Teoriya mekhaniki gruntov (Theoretical soil mechanics). Translated from English, Gosstroiizdat, Moscow.

62. Troitskaya, M.N. 1945. Opredelenie nesushchei sposobnosti i modulya deformatsii gruntov (Determination of the bearing capacity and modulus of the deformation of soils). *Stroitel'stvo Dorog*, No. 12.

63. Ul'yanov, N.A. 1962. Osnovy teorii i rascheta kolesnogo dvizhitelya zemleroinykh mashin (Fundamentals of the theory and design of wheeled excavators). Mashgiz, Moscow.

64. Ul'yanov, F.G. 1964. Povyshenie prokhodimosti i tyagovykh svoistv kolesnykh traktorov na pnevmaticheskikh shinakh (Improving the off-the-road mobility and traction properties of wheeled tractors). *Mashinostroenie*, Moscow.

202

65. Fal'kevich, B.S. 1963. Teoriya avtomobilya (Theory of automobiles). Mashgiz, Moscow.
66. Farobin, Ya.E. 1970. Teoriya povorota transportnykh mashin (Theory of the cornering of transport machines). *Mashinostroenie*, Moscow.
67. Tsentral'nye institut prognozov. Spravochnik agrogidrologicheskikh svoistv pochv SSSR (Agro-hydrological properties of soils of the USSR). Gidrometeoizdat, Moscow. 1953.
68. Tsukerberg, S.M., et al. 1960. Shiny dlya avtomobilei povyshennoi prokhodimosti (Tires for high mobility off-the-road automobiles). Goskhimizdat, Moscow.
69. Tsytovich, N.A. 1968. Mekhanika gruntov (Soil mechanics). *Vysshaya Shkola*, Moscow.
70. Chudakov, E.A. 1947. Kachenie avtomobil'nogo kolesa (Rolling of an automobile wheel). Mashgiz, Moscow.
71. Sharikyan, Yu.E'. and S.G. Vol'skii. 1967. Tseplenie shin pri dvizhenii avtomobilya po sukhomu pesku (Adhesion of tires during the locomotion of an automobile on dry sand). *Avtomobil'naya Promyshlennost'*, No. 12.
72. Shitov, V.I. 1960. K voprosu raionirovaniya lesnykh ploshchadei po nesushchei sposobnosti gruntov (The zoning of forest areas based on the load bearing capacity of soils). *Trudy TsNIIME'*, Vol. XV, No. 4.
73. Yarmashevich, Yu.I. 1963. Vliyanie kinematicheskogo nesootvetstviya na tyagovye pokazateli traktora s chetyr'mya vedushchimi kolesami (Influence of kinematic imbalance on the traction characteristics of four-wheel drive tractors). *Izvestiya Vuzov. Mashinostroenie*, No. 8.
74. Bekker, M.G. 1956. Theory of Land Locomotion (The mechanics of vehicle mobility).
75. Bekker, M.G. 1960. Off-the-Road Locomotion. The University of Michigan Press.
76. Bekker, M.G. 1960. Track and Wheel Evaluation. *Machine Design*, January 21.
77. Bischoff, T.I. 1962. Mobility and Tactical Vehicle Design, *Automobile Industries*, Vol. 126.
78. Cooper, D.H. 1958. Die Verteilung der Seitenfuhrungkraft und der Schlupfes in der Bodenführungsfläche von Reifen. *Kautschuk und Gummi*, S.W.T. 273.
79. Domsch, M. 1954. Forderungen des Ackerbodens an Schleppezgewichte und Schlepperreifen. *Deutsche Agrartechnik*, Vol. 4, No. 12.
80. Ogorkiewicz, R.M. 1963. Articulated Off-the-Road Vehicles. *Engineer*, Vol. 216, No. 5629.
81. Pohls, E. and H. Crowth. 1955. Untersuchungen über die Eindringtiefe des Schlepperraddrückes. *Deutsche Landwirtshaft*, Vol. 6, No. 3.
82. Rotta, I. 1949. Zur statik des Luftreifens. *Ingenieur-Archiv*, Vol. 17, Nos. 1–2.